A BABY'S STORY

A BABY'S STORY

A remarkable photographic account of a baby's first year

DR NICOLA McCLURE AND JANE BURTON

MICHAEL JOSEPH
LONDON

MICHAEL JOSEPH LTD

Published by the Penguin Group
27 Wrights Lane, London W8 5TZ, England
Viking Penguin Inc., 40 West 23rd Street, New York, New York 10010, USA
Penguin Books Australia Ltd, Ringwood, Victoria, Australia
Penguin Books Canada Ltd, 2801 John Street, Markham, Ontario, Canada L3R 1B4
Penguin Books (NZ) Ltd, 182–190 Wairau Road, Auckland 10, New Zealand

Penguin Books Ltd, Registered Offices: Harmondsworth, Middlesex, England

First published by Michael Joseph Ltd 1989

Text copyright © Dr Nicola McClure 1989
Photographs copyright © Jane Burton 1989
This edition copyright © Eddison Sadd Editions 1989

A CIP catalogue record for this book is available from the British Library.

ISBN 0 7181 3101 0

AN EDDISON · SADD EDITION
Edited, designed and produced by
Eddison Sadd Editions Limited
St Chad's Court, 146B King's Cross Road,
London WC1X 9DH

Phototypeset by Bookworm Typesetting, Manchester, England
Origination by Columbia Offset, Singapore
Printed and bound in Yugoslavia

CONTENTS

FOREWORD 6

CHAPTER ONE

THE NEW ARRIVAL 8

CHAPTER TWO

SITTING UP 22

CHAPTER THREE

PART OF THE FAMILY 42

CHAPTER FOUR

OUT AND ABOUT 66

CHAPTER FIVE

WALKING TALL 90

CHAPTER SIX

THE GROWING CHILD 106

CHART YOUR BABY'S STORY 128

FURTHER READING 132

INDEX 133

ACKNOWLEDGEMENTS 136

FOREWORD

Babies come charged with energy, chock-full of curiosity – packed with potential to change the world. In every country and culture, whether parents are poor or well off, in the right nurturing environment a baby learns about and gives love, trusts and in turn gives confidence to those caring for him, through five exquisite senses discovers the richness and variety of stuffs and textures, smells, tastes, colours, darkness, shadow and light, and savours the comfort and security that comes from being held close in loving arms.

Once on the move, each toddler becomes an explorer in a new country, an inventor, a mimic, a mountaineer, acrobat, clown and entertainer, an artist, engineer, skilled linguist and scientist.

The lively and beautiful photographs in this book, and a mother's own diary of his development, record a little boy's first fourteen months and reveal the excitement that comes from carefully observing the development of neuro-muscular coordination, the unfolding of personality and patterns of communication and the building of powerful human bonds of love and trust.

Life is the greatest adventure there is. In these pages one baby sets out on it with vivacity, courage, and bubbling with sheer joy.

As the expected date of delivery draws near, the waiting is almost over. While the first part of pregnancy seems to pass by in a flurry of ante-natal appointments, the last few weeks tend to drag – even though Gemma, Annette's eighteen-month-old daughter, has finally understood that mummy has a baby inside her tummy.

CHAPTER ONE

THE NEW ARRIVAL

As a mother cradles her baby in her arms she will probably be feeling a profound relief that the strain of the delivery is over. But above all, she will be thankful that her baby is normal and healthy. Not all mothers fall instantly in love with the little bundle in their arms – some women do, but others prefer older babies. This is understandable, because a baby may not look particularly appealing straight after delivery. At that moment the mother may be tired and a bit mixed up, with one powerful emotion jostling another. It is normal for mothers to experience all sorts of different feelings and conflicting emotions at this stage. There will be plenty of time in the coming years for a mother's relationship with her child to develop and grow.

Her partner, too, will be relieved that all has gone well and that both mother and baby are safe. He will probably feel proud of and very protective towards them – and possibly a bit left out as he has not been the active partner in the birth.

But if both parents feel relieved, how does the new baby feel? The answer is that we don't know for sure. We can make a few assumptions, though. He has been through a lot already. He has just left a warm, watery, safe place and has been pushed out into a colder, noisier, brighter outside world. A number of vitally important changes have taken place inside him, enabling him to live an independent life. His lungs have filled with air for the first time and the umbilical cord has been cut. The delivery must be a shock – perhaps the greatest shock of his life; but it is one for which he is instinctively prepared . . .

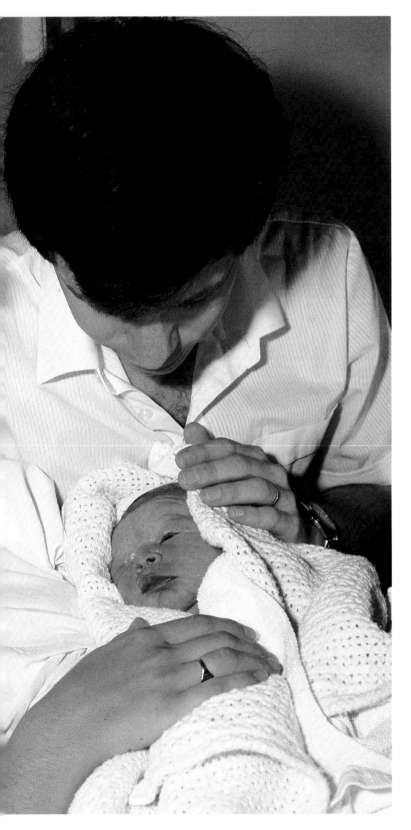

Annette and Jason holding Dean, moments after his delivery. Dean has been cleaned up a little and wrapped in a soft baby blanket. His eyes are open and he is already looking at his mother's face.

AUTHOR'S NOTE
In this book I have used the pronoun 'he' throughout the text. All my observations of child growth and development, however, apply equally to both girls and boys.

FIRST DAYS

No wonder they call it labour – giving birth really is very hard work indeed. The mother is well-prepared, though, since she has discussed pain relief, breathing control and the mechanics of birth at her ante-natal classes. First come the contractions: slight and infrequent in the beginning, but building up in intensity until they are powerful enough to gradually dilate the cervix and push the baby along the birth canal. The contractions are painful, there is no denying it, but there are many ways of coping with the pain. A mother can decide to try a mixture of gas and air, or maybe – if labour is protracted – take the advice of the doctor or midwife and have an epidural anaesthetic. Some mothers, though, find that like Annette they can manage with no artificial pain relief at all. Pushing, the second stage of labour, starts when the cervix is fully dilated and the mother feels the urge to push. Soon, the baby's head emerges – with the help of a mirror, the mother can actually see this happening. She can certainly hear his first cry and feel his warm, soft, moist body as he is placed on her tummy immediately after the delivery. At that moment all the waiting and pain of the last few hours seems worthwhile.

Cutting the cord

The newborn baby usually starts breathing at once and does not need to be smacked on the bottom – unless, that is, his nose and mouth are obstructed by mucus. The midwife checks the baby carefully, noting his colour, breathing, his general appearance and that he cries normally. If she is at all worried, or if the delivery has been complicated, the paediatrician looks at the baby as well.

A number of changes take place in the baby's heart and lungs at birth, all of which allow him to breathe independently. As a result, the umbilical cord can now be clamped and cut, severing the connection between mother and baby. After a few days, the remnants of the cord shrivel up and drop off, leaving a scar at the navel which becomes the belly button.

Newborn babies are usually covered in a greasy film, called vernix, and may also be smeared with blood, particularly if the mother has had a small tear or surgical cut (an episiotomy) during the delivery. Some women prefer to have their babies cleaned up and wrapped in a soft blanket before they hold them; others like to touch their babies immediately, and ask for them to be delivered directly on to their tummies so that they can hold them before the cord is cut.

The newborn baby is usually put to the breast straightaway: it seems the natural thing to do. The baby feels the soft warmth of his mother's breast, smells the milk and opens his mouth ready to suckle when the nipple brushes his lips. Suckling triggers the release of the hormone oxytocin, which causes the womb to contract and helps the delivery of the placenta. So, in the first moments of the new life, mother and baby are already working as a team.

The first few days of life are generally spent in hospital – unless of course, the mother has had her baby at home – though some mothers prefer to go home the same day. In a maternity hospital, there are always midwives around to help and answer questions, while at home you may find yourself entirely alone with a new baby to look after. It can be a bit frightening. He is so small, delicate and helpless, how will you know what he wants? The answer is that

---

DIARY 10TH AUGUST

When he was born Dean soon began to cry and protest. At first, he did not seem interested in my breast at all; he soon started to suckle, however, and continued to feed and doze for the rest of the morning.

I had thought that after my bath I would be discharged from the hospital and allowed to go home. But the midwife decided that I should stay because as Dean was such a big baby, she wanted to take more glucose readings later.

The midwife has clamped the cord in two places, and is just about to cut it, _right_. The cord does not contain any nerve fibres, so the procedure is completely painless.

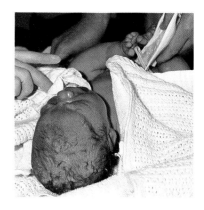

After being cut, the cord is clamped with a sterile plastic clip like a clothes peg, _middle_.

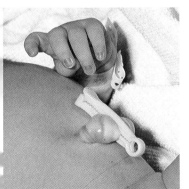

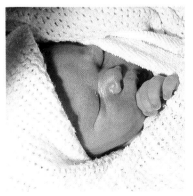

Not long after delivery, Dean is feeding happily at Annette's breast, *above*. At first, Dean receives colostrum, a rich creamy food that also contains protective antibodies. After a few days the milk 'comes in' – the breasts feel heavy, uncomfortable and full.

Some newborn babies like to be swaddled, or wrapped up firmly, in clean, soft blankets, *left*.

11

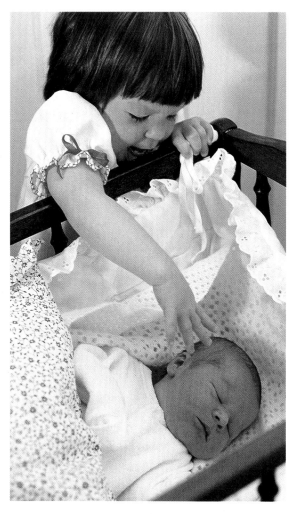

Gemma is excited that at last the new baby is in his crib, *above*. She tries to poke and prod him, entranced by his appearance.

you will know, and you will be able to cope. A new baby has remarkably few needs: food, warmth, love and security; all of which the mother will be able to provide easily. Babies are also surprisingly good at making their needs known. They cry. Crying is a baby's only means of communication, and the noise he makes has nothing to do with emotional distress. He cries because he is hungry, cold, wet or lonely and his mother responds to the cry. Within days she will be reassured to find that she seems to know instinctively from his cry what he wants. Never be afraid to respond for fear that you will spoil him. This is nonsense. It is not possible to spoil a very young baby, who will only cry for a reason. In fact, the reverse is almost true. If you go quickly to your crying baby, attend to his needs, soothe him and settle him down again, he will come to understand that you are always nearby looking after him, and will cry less, rather than more, often.

The whole family

A new baby in the house means a major upheaval for the rest of the family. The mother will be tired and may be low in spirits after the birth, and the other members of the family may be feeling a bit jealous of the new arrival, who takes up so much of her time. Of course, they are delighted with the baby as well, and can be very loving, gentle and generous towards him. But a certain amount of jealousy is entirely normal. It can be minimized by involving the whole family in his care: fathers can want to bathe and cuddle babies just as much as mothers, for example, while older children can help with nappy changes, push prams and help look after the new baby.

DIARY 12TH AUGUST

Yesterday I was allowed home and as yet Dean is showing no signs of any routine. He is feeding from me all the time, or so it seems. He is a very wakeful little chap, probably tending to wake up every couple of hours, because Gemma keeps waking him up, screaming in his ear or patting his feet as he sits on the dining room table in his carrycot. He is a very windy baby; he holds onto his wind like grim death and then seems to suffer from it until we can get him settled to sleep again.

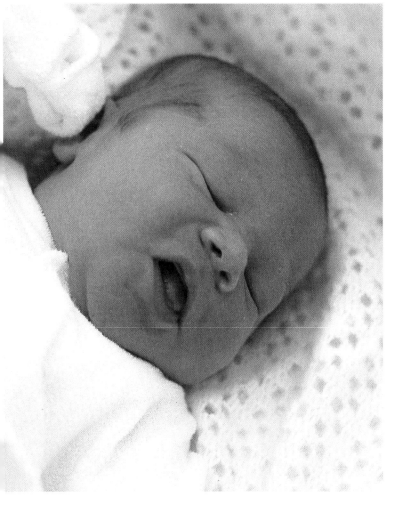

NEWBORN BABIES

● Newborn babies sleep on and off for most of the day. They are usually put to sleep on their tummies or side, but make sure that there is not a pillow to hamper the baby's breathing.

● Babies wake to feed frequently. The feeding routine settles down over the first few weeks: breast-fed babies tend to demand feeding every three hours or so – though many prefer to feed at the breast much more frequently; bottle-fed babies can often go for four hours between feeds. This difference is because a baby digests breast milk more quickly than cow's milk.

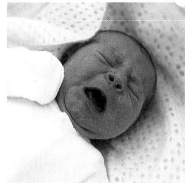

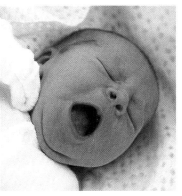

Dean is just waking from a deep sleep, *left*, with a huge yawn. Newborn babies spend most of their time asleep, waking every so often to be fed. At first he whimpers a little, *above*, making sucking motions with his mouth and tongue; then, when he is properly awake, Dean opens his mouth, *above right* and gives a good hearty cry to let Annette know that he is hungry.

THE REFLEXES

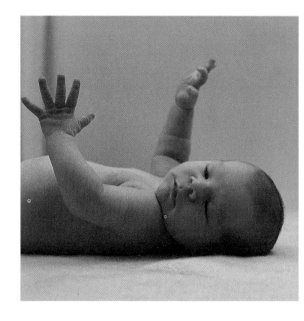

The newborn baby exhibits certain reflexes; that is, automatic, unconscious responses to stimuli. Some of these, such as blinking, persist throughout life, while others disappear after the first few months. Some reflexes are remnants of primitive responses designed to help the newborn survive. If, for example, you place your finger in the palm of the baby's hand, he will grasp it firmly – in our distant evolutionary past, this response, the grasp reflex, would have helped a small animal to cling to its mother's fur. As the baby grows and the nervous system develops, most primitive reflexes disappear, to be replaced by more complex behavioural responses.

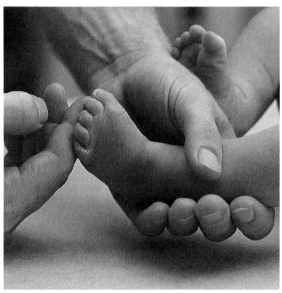

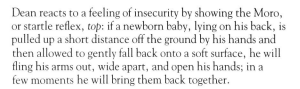

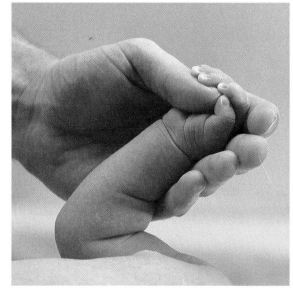

Dean reacts to a feeling of insecurity by showing the Moro, or startle reflex, *top*: if a newborn baby, lying on his back, is pulled up a short distance off the ground by his hands and then allowed to gently fall back onto a soft surface, he will fling his arms out, wide apart, and open his hands; in a few moments he will bring them back together.

Two beautiful demonstrations of the grasp reflex: the picture, *left*, shows how the toes can be made to flex and curl over, in a form of grasp reflex, when the sole of the foot is touched lightly. The newborn's fingers tightly grip anything that touches the palm, *above*.

When a new baby is held upright on a firm surface he appears to be trying to walk, *right*. In fact, this is the stepping reflex, seen when pressure on the sole of the foot causes the leg to bend and then straighten. This reflex usually disappears before the baby is six months old.

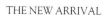

A BABY'S SKIN

Often, newborn babies are not a pretty sight and they may even look rather alarming. Instead of being plump and pretty they come in all shapes and sizes, depending on their age and the way in which they have been delivered.

Not surprisingly, premature babies tend to be small and rather skinny, as they have not been in the womb long enough to lay down a covering of fat beneath the skin. They may still be covered in a layer of soft, downy hair called lanugo. This hair covers all babies whilst they develop in the womb but has usually disappeared by the time they are born; otherwise it rubs off in a couple of days. Overdue babies sometimes have peeling skin, particularly on their hands and feet, but this soon disappears leaving perfect skin underneath. But most babies are born covered in vernix. This is a greasy substance, secreted

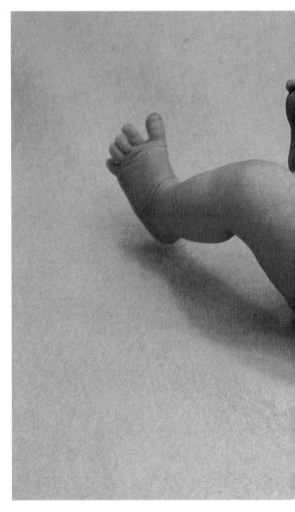

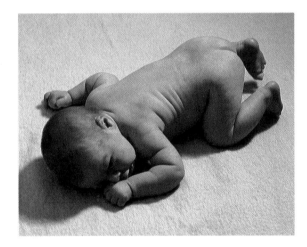

Dean lying prone, or on his front, *left*. He has arranged himself in the characteristic way of a small baby in this position: his knees are drawn up under his tummy, his bottom is high, his arms are bent and his head is turned to one side. In the picture *above*, Dean is lying supine, or on his back. His head is turned to one side with the leg on that side stretched out. Both arms are flexed at the elbow.

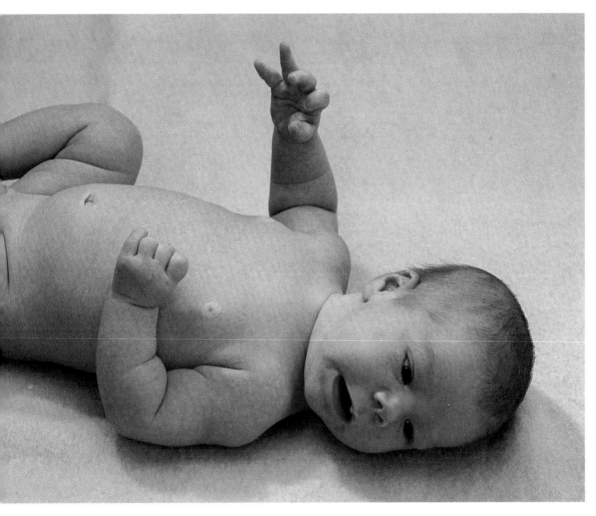

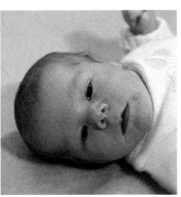

Like many babies, Dean has spots and
rashes from time to time, *left*. They
may be unsightly, but they are quite
harmless and soon disappear.

by the glands in the skin, which protected the baby while it was lying in amniotic fluid in the womb. Vernix tends to accumulate in skin folds, but can easily be wiped or washed off. A surprising amount of blood may also be smeared over the newborn. Don't worry – this often occurs during delivery. The following paragraphs mention other aspects of your new baby's appearance that may seem unusual.

New babies often go yellow during the first week, as a result of temporary jaundice. What happens is that the baby's immature liver cannot cope with its job of breaking down fetal haemoglobin – a component of red blood cells – and bilirubin, one of the breakdown products, starts to accumulate, turning the skin a yellowish colour. The problem normally clears up on its own, but if it persists, the baby is treated with ultra-violet light, which breaks down the bilirubin.

You may notice that your new baby's head tends to be rather large compared to the size of his body. It may also be an odd, elongated shape, depending on the type of delivery. Babies born by Caesarian section, for example, often have regular, beautifully shaped heads, while those that pass along the birth canal tend to have slightly elongated heads. Sometimes there is also a small, soft swelling at the back of the baby's head, called a caput.

The reason for these changes in shape is that the bones of the baby's skull are able to move and they overlap a little during delivery, to help the head pass through the birth canal. This process, called moulding, is absolutely routine and does not affect the brain at all. Eventually, the shape of the head will return to normal, though this may take quite some while.

There is no rule as to what a baby's hair looks like. Some babies are born with masses of thick, dark hair while others have such fair, fine hair that they seem to be bald. Occasionally the scalp is covered with a layer of scurf, known as cradle cap, which is made up of greasy brownish scales. This may be unsightly, but it is not a serious problem and can be cleared up quickly by the use of special shampoos.

Most babies are born with blue eyes, and the colour only changes – if it is going to – over the next few months.

Birthmarks, spots and rashes

Some birthmarks, of course, are permanent. But the vast majority are harmless, disappearing after a year or so. In this category come Stork's Beak marks: reddish marks on the forehead, bridge of the nose, upper eyelids or nape of the neck. On the other hand, strawberry naevi, bright red marks on the face or scalp, usually reduce in size and disappear.

Young babies usually have a few shiny white spots on the nose and cheeks during the first few weeks. These are nothing to do with feeding, even though they are often called milk spots. In fact, they are probably due to temporarily blocked glands in the skin. They will go away, and should not be squeezed.

Most babies suffer from nappy rash during their first year. It is generally caused by prolonged contact with dirty nappies. A mild attack can be treated with creams bought at the chemist, but more severe, persistent bouts may involve thrush and need a soothing anti-fungal cream. Prevention is best, though: change nappies frequently; use a barrier cream to protect wet skin; and avoid plastic pants.

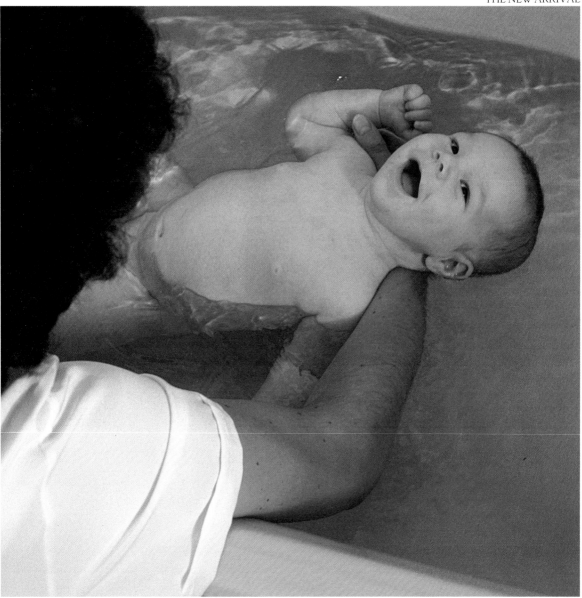

Dean clearly loves his bath. Annette started by testing the temperature of the water and then placed Dean carefully in it. She is bathing him with her right arm under his body to give support, and has a firm hold on his right shoulder.

There is no real need to go to the expense of buying a special baby bath, as this photograph shows. A baby can just as easily be bathed in an adult bath, or even the kitchen sink. But wherever you bath your baby, great care is essential.

DIARY 20TH AUGUST

Because he was five days late, Dean's skin was a bit dry when he was born, but that seems to have improved by rubbing Vaseline on his skin and also putting some baby oil in his bath. I have only given him a couple of baths so far.

He is getting little red spots on his face, which look much worse when he gets himself all het up. He seems to have a bit of a temper – when he is displeased he can scream and scream and as he calms himself the spots go down again.

ENJOYING YOUR BABY

Parents and babies spend the first few months getting used to each other. Mothers soon learn what their new baby wants when he cries and become expert at providing it. Feeding, bathing and nappy changing all become easier with time and life in general becomes less fraught as a routine is established to suit everybody. For his part, the baby knows that he will be comforted and fed or changed when he cries, and so becomes contented and secure in his new environment. Babies adore attention and delight in love and approval. At about this time they are awake for longer periods throughout the day and, with any luck, sleep for more of the night – though they may wake up frequently.

This means that you are not quite so tired as you were and have more energy to play with your baby. From about four to six weeks, a baby starts to smile back at you when you cuddle him and make happy cooing noises when you talk to him softly. He will turn his head towards you when you talk, and will usually stop crying when you soothe him. Looking after him becomes much more rewarding.

Take the time to sit and play with your baby; after all, you are his first playmate. Yours is the face, the voice and the smell he knows and loves best, and he loves to be near you and be the centre of your attention. You will not spoil him by loving, cuddling and talking to him, but help him to learn and to grow in confidence as well as in size.

Brothers and sisters
Older children, too, soon come to accept the new arrival, though there may have been a certain amount of resentment and jealousy at first. They may need a good deal of reassurance and explanation that you love them just as much now as you did before the new arrival; and that they too were once so tiny and that you fed and looked after them in exactly the same way.

Older children who are secure in the knowledge of their parents' love are likely to be more generous towards the baby and less jealous – though there will be the odd tantrum now and again. Try to set aside some time for them, when you can ask about their day and play with them alone. Make a space for them beside you when you feed the baby, as Annette has done with Gemma, and let them help you look after their new brother.

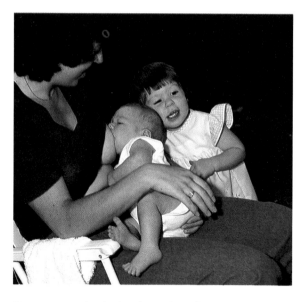

Dean enjoying his feed in the garden, *above*, on a warm summer evening. Gemma shares the experience – a good way of making sure that she knows she's still important, too. Afterwards, Dean feels sleepy and contented, *right*, and Annette takes the time to have a quiet cuddle and reflect on how much he has grown during six weeks.

DIARY 19TH SEPTEMBER

He is a very alert little boy, more so than Gemma when she was born. I am not sure exactly how much he can see but he seems to look at me intently and he loves bright lights.

He does not posset, appears to really enjoy his food and keeps it all down. I hope I can keep him satisfied for some time to come.

Gemma is very good with him, not at all rough or vindictive towards him. If anything, she is reacting towards me rather than to Dean. Whenever he cries she comes and tells me and she surprised us the other day by picking up his dirty nappy and putting it in the pedal bin.

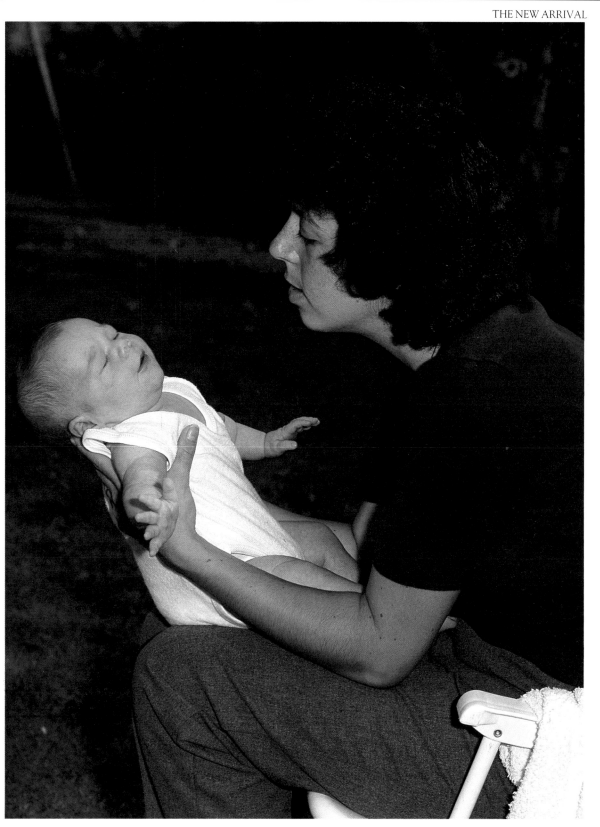

CHAPTER TWO

SITTING UP

By the beginning of the third month, the baby has rounded out and has lost his rather battered, newborn look. His head is a more regular shape and he has more hair. In fact, he is beginning to look more the way a baby is generally supposed to look.

By now, he is very much a member of the family, and everyone is becoming aware of his likes and dislikes. Mother and baby feel close to each other, and more confident and settled with one other. She may not have fallen in love with him at birth, but after these few months together they have established a very close relationship. Although the baby is still totally dependent on his mother for food, warmth and shelter, he is much more responsive . . . and that makes all the hard work of caring for his needs worthwhile.

Like most babies of this age, Dean is learning every day, and gaining in confidence as he goes along. He is heavier and stronger and his body is much less floppy than at birth. This is because he is learning to control the various parts of his body. This process begins at the head and continues downwards. He moves a great deal more than he did – kicking his legs and playing with his hands.

He is interested in everything and follows Annette's movements around the room, often turning to the sound of her voice. He has begun to understand what is going on around him, becoming very excited when he knows that he is going to be fed or bathed – he coos, chuckles and squeals with delight and wriggles in expectation. Dean has only been alive for nearly three months, but he has already learned a great deal.

Dean is quite happy being held up in a sitting position on Annette's lap. He has good head control and is able to hold his head up easily. His back is firm and straight at the top but there is still a lumbar curve – low down on the spine. He looks interested and alert and is clearly delighted to be the centre of attention.

A WORLD IN HIS HANDS

The ability to use our hands is one of our most important skills, and it distinguishes us from the rest of the animal kingdom. As humans evolved from apes, they lost the ability to run on all fours and to hold things with their feet. Legs grew longer, as our posture became upright, and arms grew shorter. But, above all, it was the development of the hands as precision tools, capable of a wide range of movements, yet with fine control, that contributed to our separate, and superior evolution.

So the hands occupy a central role in a baby's development, from about three months onwards. In the newborn, the fists are kept tightly closed with the fingers bent over into the palm. But as the baby grows older, the hands open out. Eventually, he discovers his fingers. From about ten weeks onwards the baby brings his arms together in front of him and stares at them, while playing with his fingers and clasping and unclasping his hands.

This is the first step in the development of hand-eye coordination, itself an essential prerequisite to reaching for objects. Later – at around six months – he will learn to grasp things. At first it is a crude motion usually requiring both his hands, but by nine months it becomes more delicate, involving the thumb and forefinger of one hand.

Dean happily sucking his left hand, *above*. Very young babies often suck their fingers or a thumb – in fact they can be seen doing so even inside the womb, on an ultrasound scan. Initially they probably suck things for comfort, but later on they use their mouths to learn about things. They explore the shape, texture and taste of objects with their lips and tongue, so it is quite natural for them to put everything they can find in their mouths.

Dean is holding his two hands together in front of him, *above*, with the palms facing each other and the fingers interlocking. He will play like this, quite happily, for long periods. He gazes intently at his hands, starting to learn where they are in relation to the rest of his body and what he can do with them. In three months' time, when he is six months old, he will be able to reach for toys, pick them up and pass them backwards and forwards from hand to hand.

At the age of three months, Dean can hold a rattle, *below*. He has a crude palmar grasp, but cannot put things down voluntarily. Instead he simply opens his hand and the object falls to the floor.

A HEAD START

The newborn baby is relatively floppy and cannot control the position of his head. This is hardly surprising, because the head is heavy and the muscles of the baby's neck are weak. So when the baby is held with his tummy parallel to a bed, in the position known as ventral suspension, his head drops down below the level of his body. By the same token, a baby's head will flop back if it is not supported when he is held in your arms, making the baby look very uncomfortable.

By the age of six weeks, head control is beginning to develop and when held in ventral suspension by a hand underneath his tummy, he can momentarily hold his head up in the same plane as the rest of his body. When lying asleep on his tummy, a baby of this age lies in the fetal position, with his knees drawn up under his trunk so that his bottom is held high off the cot; when he wakes up, his bottom is fairly low on the cot and his legs are partially or intermittently stretched out. He may raise his head momentarily and look ahead of him, but cannot hold this position for very long.

Head high

By three months, though, head control has improved enormously. When lying on his tummy on the floor he can raise his head, shoulders and the upper part of his chest off the floor, taking their weight on his forearms. In this position he can look in front of him and also see a little of what is going on at either side, while kicking his legs. He will quite obviously be pleased with his achievement, cooing and gurgling away to himself.

Being able to hold your head up when lying on

Dean is supporting the weight of his head and shoulders on his forearms, and looking around to see what is going on. Ever curious, he is scratching at the rug with his left hand, assessing its coarse, hairy texture.

your tummy is important, because so much more can be seen. Without this ability, humans would have a very limited visual field compared with other animals, because of the position of our eyes. In the early days of man's evolution this means of extending the visual field would have been vital to survival.

Some babies don't enjoy lying on their tummies, and scream with frustration when left in this position. Just like adults, babies have preferences, so there is no need to worry if this happens. Instead, try placing babies that react in this way on their backs, ideally propped up in a well-designed baby seat – a wide variety of safe, ingeniously constructed models are available – so that they can see around them and move their arms and legs freely. All babies enjoy a change of position.

This will also give you a chance to see the new improvement in head control, which is very noticeable when a baby is pulled up into the sitting position. The head lags behind just after birth and flops backwards, but by six weeks the baby starts to hold his head up in line with his body when it has reached the vertical; after this the head flops forwards.

Control from the top

By three months, hardly any head lag can be seen, and the improvement does not stop with the head. This is because a baby's development of neuromuscular control starts at the top and works downwards. So control of the shoulders and upper torso quickly follows the ability to control the head.

Later, control spreads downwards to include the lower back, or lumbar, region. When a newborn baby is held in the sitting position the back forms a smooth rounded curve, with the head flopped forward. Three months later, however, the upper part of the back is straight, though there is still a curve in the lower, lumbar region of the spine. By the time a baby is six months old, his back will be straight and he will probably be able to sit by himself for short periods.

Annette pulling Dean to the sitting position, *above*, when one month old. He has very little head control at this age, so his head lags behind his body. He is also demonstrating the grasp reflex, by grabbing his mother's thumbs firmly when they are placed in the palm of his hand. When pulled right up to sit, Dean's back will form a smooth curve, with his head flopping over forwards and almost touching the ground in front of him.

By three months, Dean has very little head lag, *right*, when pulled to sit by his father, Jason. When held sitting, the top half of his back is straight while the lower part is still curved.

DIARY 24TH OCTOBER

When Dean was six days old I started to use a sling to be able to carry him around and have him close while I did the housework. He loved the vacuum cleaner, the noise sent him straight to sleep.

He just loves being picked up and carried around so that he can see his environment from a shoulder view. Now that he is nearly twelve weeks, his neck is getting stronger and he is starting to try and lift himself up. You have to be very careful because when he is over your shoulder, he can suddenly lift himself up and throw himself back. He has got very strong legs and he tries to kick when his nappy is being changed.

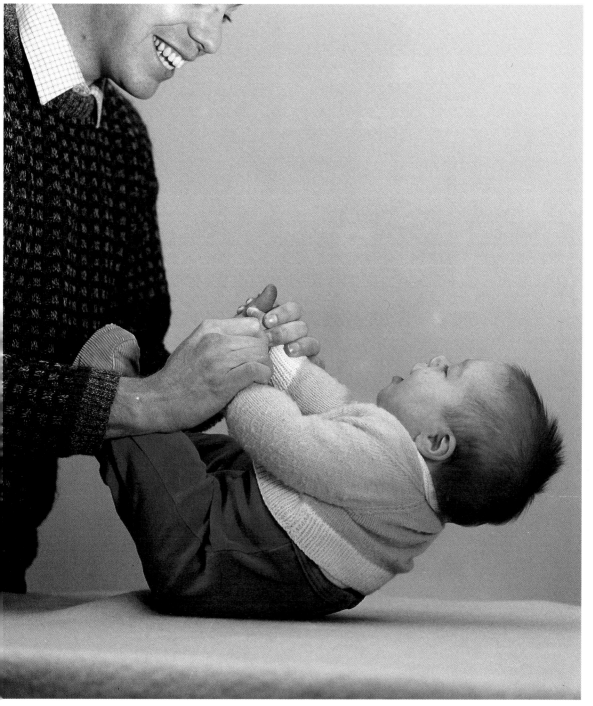

THE SENSES

Babies are inquisitive. They love to know what is going on around them, and to watch, listen, smell, feel and taste everything they can. So babies assimilate a huge amount of information during the first year of life, and this process forms the basis of learning. Before they can even make a start on this lengthy business, however, they have to be able to perceive the information they are to absorb. This is where the five senses come in: sight, hearing, smell, taste and touch. We take them for granted, but for a baby they open up a whole new world of knowledge.

Sight
Babies can see quite clearly from birth. They focus best on objects about twenty-three centimetres (9 in) from their faces, anything else appearing slightly blurred in the background. This is the same as being rather 'short-sighted' in adult life. However, babies can see in colour, and there is good evidence to show that they have an idea of distance and perspective, right from birth.

Usually, the first thing that a newborn baby sees is his mother's face. He is fascinated by it, and is more interested in a human face than in anything else. Often, he will imitate mother's facial expressions – opening his mouth if she opens her's, for example, demonstrating that he can not only see her face but judge her expression.

This is intriguing, because it suggests that a newborn baby, who has never had the opportunity to look at himself in the mirror, knows he has a mouth that will open in the same way as his mother's. It would seem that he recognizes that he is a member of the same race as his mother, right from the start.

A newborn baby is 'short-sighted'. He can see objects that are close to the front of his face clearly enough, *right*, but everything else is a bit of a blur. This means that he can focus on his mother's face while feeding and cuddling, so it is hardly surprising that the human face becomes his favourite sight.

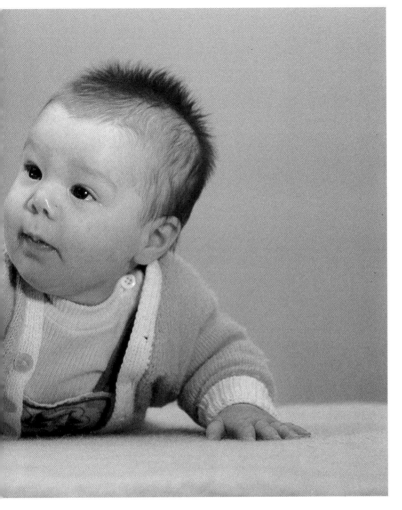

DIARY 29TH OCTOBER

Dean can see much further now and he seems to know the sound of my voice. If someone else is holding him and I come into the room and say something to him, he immediately turns and acknowledges me. He talks a lot; he is a proper little chatterbox when he gets going, chatter, chatter, chatter; he gets louder and louder trying to compete with me because I think he hears me talking with Gemma and he wants to do it too.

He and Gemma are tolerating each other much better now as Gemma has realized that he is becoming bigger and stronger and so more fun to play with.

He likes to be on his tummy and if you put a few things in front of him he will lift his head right up and look at them for quite a while.

Now that Dean can raise his head and shoulders from the ground, *above*, he can see what is going on around him – even though it's all a bit out of focus. Nevertheless, he often finds something to delight him, *above right*.

As he can focus clearly over a short distance, Dean finds plenty to occupy his attention, in this case, Gemma, *left*. But Annette, as always, is present to make sure that nothing gets out of hand.

Hearing

Babies can also hear extremely well at birth. In fact, they can hear the higher frequencies of sound even better than adults – this might explain why they find some sounds particularly upsetting, when adults can hardly hear them at all. Just as a newborn baby is fascinated by the human face, he is also intensely interested in human voices – especially those of his mother and father.

Smell and taste

Babies can smell and taste at birth, though their preferences are not necessarily the same as those of an adult. Indeed, they may even appear to like some

Dean reaching for his rattle with his right hand, *above*. Having seen the toy, he is learning how to judge where it is, and where his hand is in relation to it.

smells which adults find revolting. Taste is a different matter, however. Nearly all babies like sweet things at birth, and individual preferences usually become apparent during weaning.

The sixth sense

Proprioception, or the sixth sense, is also known as joint-position sense. It tells us where the various parts of our body are in relation to the other parts. As adults, we know instinctively where our hands and feet are, and do not have to think before we move them. But a new baby does not instinctively know where his hands are. He eventually 'finds' them – first by touch at about six weeks or so, and later by sight.

A baby of three months, for example, will hold a rattle when it is placed in his hand, but cannot look at it at the same time. He may even hit himself in the face with it, showing that he cannot yet coordinate vision and hand movement. The noise made by the rattle may attract his attention, however, and cause him to look at his hand and the rattle it holds.

A baby learns to reach in stages. At about three months he will lash out at things and hit them with the flat of his hand. A month or so later he reaches for things more delicately, first looking at his own hand and judging where it is, then looking at the object. He moves his hand and repeats this process until he eventually grasps the toy.

By six months, however, he knows exactly where his hand is and he can also see the toy clearly. As a result he reaches out to grab it smoothly and accurately. This technique, called visually associated reaching, also shows his developing hand-eye coordination. Now he can get what he wants.

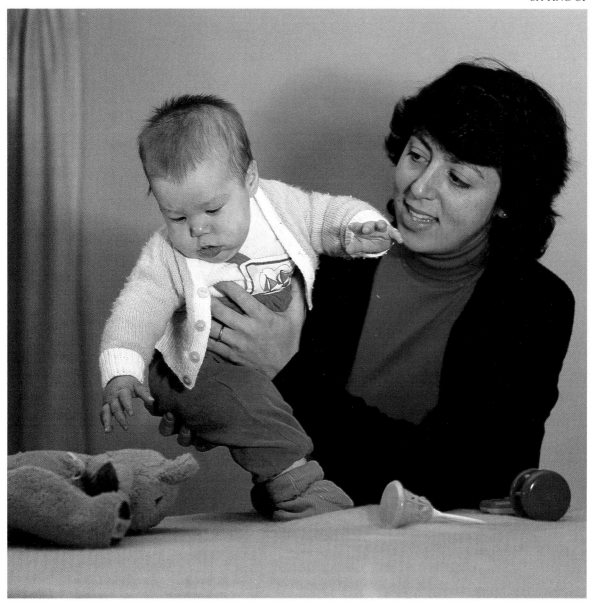

TOYS

Toys are an important part of a baby's life at this age. He needs colours to develop sight, rattles to train hearing and things to encourage him to reach.

● Toys or play objects must not have any sharp edges or small parts that can fall off, and must be large enough that they cannot be swallowed – he will put all toys in his mouth.

● Toys should be washable, and not stuffed with or painted with any toxic materials.

● There should be enough toys so that the baby does not lack stimulation nor lose interest, yet not so many that he cannot concentrate on any one toy.

● Mobiles are an ideal first toy and are cheap and easy to make. Place one about thirty centimetres (1 ft) from his face.

Dean reaching for his teddy bear, *above*. This is more difficult for him than it may appear, because he has to swivel the top half of his body around. He needs the support that he is getting from Annette.

FEEDING TIME

Breast-feeding is usually an intimate and satisfying experience for both mother and baby. It is a time when mother and baby can be close and have a few quiet moments together. The new baby loves to feed like this. He is right against your body, can smell your skin and milk and can feel your heart beating just beneath him.

However, breast-feeding can be rather tricky in the beginning, and there is a tendency for everyone to offer well-meaning, but conflicting, advice. Ignore most of it. There is no right or wrong way to feed a baby, though other breast-feeding mothers can offer some good tips. As long as the baby is gaining weight and you are well and happy, then you have both got it right.

The secret is to persevere, especially in the first few weeks when you feel you are not giving him enough milk and there is a great temptation to give him bottled milk as well. Your milk supply adjusts automatically to the baby's needs and gives him exactly what he wants. The more he suckles, the more milk you make. What is more, the milk is at just the right temperature and strength for all his needs, and, of course, it is free.

On the other hand, some women prefer not to breast-feed or find that they are unable to do so for various reasons. Bottle-feeding with the special formula feeds will provide the baby with all the nutrients he needs. And there is one positive advantage to bottle-feeding: that is, that other members of the family can feed him, freeing the mother to do something else, spend time with her children, or just have a well-earned rest.

Solids are usually introduced after about four months of milk feeding. At first they are not really solid at all, but fine purées of fruit and vegetables. The new flavours and textures should be introduced very gradually – perhaps a spoonful after the milk feed. This gives the baby time to adjust to the strange new taste and feeling in his mouth.

Babies need to learn to chew solid food to help their jaw and muscles of mastication develop properly, as well as to provide the energy they need for growth and exercise. Over a period of months, the variety and quantity of solid food can be increased, and milk feeds correspondingly reduced, so that by a year or so a baby is on a full mixed diet.

Annette is still breast-feeding Dean, *above*, and has started to give him some solids. This is usually an exciting time for a baby, because he has the best of both worlds – plenty of comforting breast-feeding as well as a variety of new flavours and textures. Unusually, though, Dean does not seem terribly happy about it, *right*.

DIARY 19TH NOVEMBER

Dean weighs seven-and-a-half kilograms (16lb 10oz) with his clothes on and everybody says he is a bonny boy. He is a fatty. His gums are getting harder and harder at the bottom and he seems to be suffering discomfort with them. He is chewing everything so some teeth could be due soon.

I have been trying him on some solids, just small portions of puréed food that we have been eating but he is not very keen and prefers Mummy. It has affected his motions; they are more solid and brown rather than very loose and bright yellow. I will keep breast-feeding him and introduce some food of my own very gradually.

THE TURNING POINT

By twenty-four weeks, Dean has just mastered the art of rolling over. He has rolled from his back on to his front and is clearly delighted with his achievement. It is a fairly complicated manoeuvre, which most babies accomplish between five and seven months. First they learn how to roll over from their tummies on to their backs. Then, a few weeks later, they manage to roll over the other way.

Annette now has to watch Dean even more closely than before and make sure that he is never left alone on a high surface – he might roll off. Changing mats are a particular hazard, as they are generally waist-high. Many babies have rolled off such mats while their mothers have turned their backs for a minute to fetch a clean nappy. Babies are much safer on a rug on the floor, where they can roll around to their heart's content. As they gain confidence, babies can roll quite quickly across the floor.

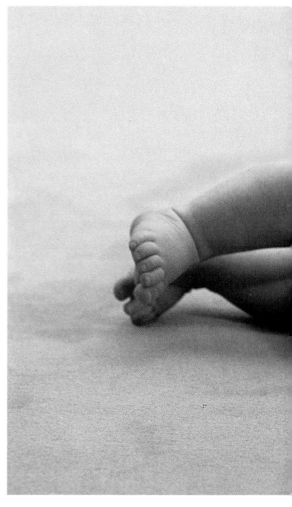

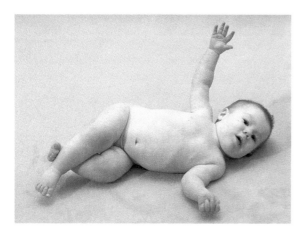

WATCHING YOUR BABY
- Make sure the sitting room is warm and spread a large rug or blanket on the floor. Undress your baby and take off his nappy so that he can move freely. Now sit back and enjoy watching him play.
- By six months most babies can sit unsupported for a few moments. They will bear their weight on their legs if held upright on a firm surface, and may bounce up and down. They can roll over – from front to back at first; later from back to front. They like to reach for things.
- Babies watch everything and will follow your

movements with their eyes. They will turn to you when you call and laugh and squeal with delight.
- Always looking, listening, touching and chewing, babies are continually learning. At the same time they are working out how to move and control their bodies prior to crawling. Almost every day they will manage some new physical effort.
- Now that your baby can move around – even if only by rolling from side to side – you must be constantly on the lookout for potential danger. Make sure that he is never left alone in any position from which he can fall.

Dean starts the movement off when lying on his back, *left*. He turns his head to one side, then swivels his hips and brings his right leg over to that side. Finally, he swings his right leg over and his trunk follows to complete the turn, *above*. Once on his tummy, he pushes up, supporting his weight on hands and knees. He is quite stable in this position, looking happily at the mess his dribble is making on the carpet. He gives the impression that he will scuttle off at any time, *right* – though, of course, he is not yet able to crawl properly.

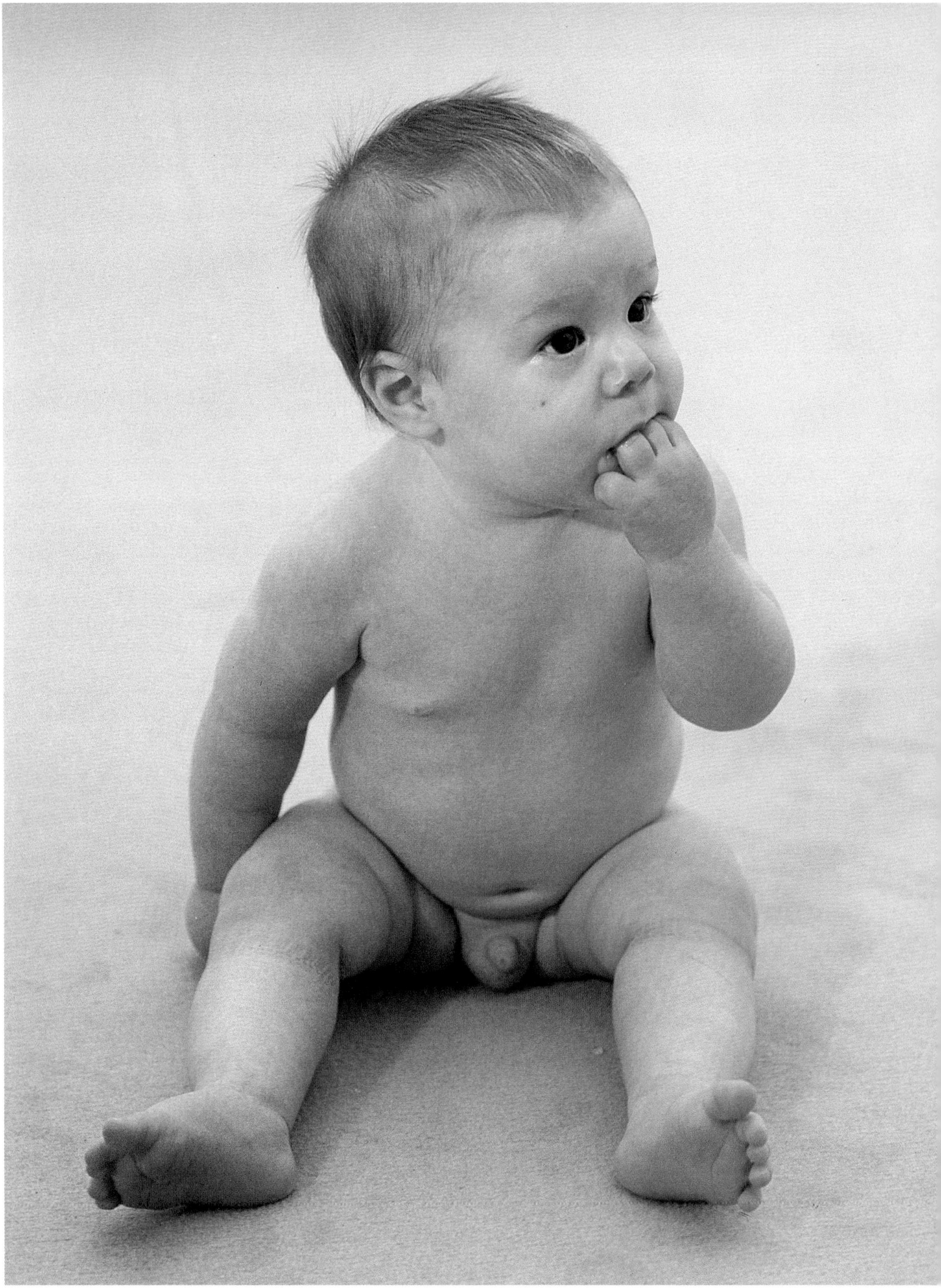

LOOK AT ME NOW

By the age of six months, most babies can sit up unaided on the floor for a few moments. But he can sit quite happily for a lot longer in a pram or special baby seat, provided that his back is well supported. In this position he will hold his head erect and look around him eagerly, interested in all the comings and goings of the people passing by him.

Perpetual motion

At this age, a baby is always on the move, throwing out his arms and his legs, and often holding his arms outstretched in a plea to be lifted up by his parents. He enjoys kicking his legs and feeling how strong

Dean's balance is so good that he can lean forwards and play with his toes without toppling over sideways, *above*. He is teething at the moment and consequently dribbles from time to time.

By six months Dean can sit on the floor by himself for several minutes, *left*. He has a good straight back and firm base, with his legs stretched out in front of him. Nevertheless, he still looks a little unsure of himself and is sucking his fingers for comfort.

they are, whether he is lying on his back or tummy. When left lying on his tummy he will push up on his outstretched arms to raise his head and upper chest, again so that he can see what is going on around him. He can also roll over from his tummy to his back, and usually throw himself the other way round as well.

If his hands are grasped, he will try to pull himself up into the sitting position. Similarly, when held with his feet on the floor he will take his weight on them, and may bounce up and down on the surface. All in all he is becoming stronger, larger and more coordinated. Although he can neither crawl nor walk at this age, he is getting ready to do both.

He is still interested in his fingers and toes and still takes everything to his mouth and sucks it. He can reach for a nearby toy and grasp it, usually with two hands though sometimes using his feet as well. He can transfer toys from one hand to the other and will manipulate them, turning them over and inspecting them carefully.

For a baby of this age, the world is a fascinating place, full of interesting sights and sounds. He desperately wants to get close to them, to find out what is behind them, and to learn from them. The trouble is that he is not yet mobile enough to move around independently and has to stay where he is put. True, he can sit up and roll over by himself, but he cannot cover much ground like that.

Frustrating as it may seem, he simply has to bide his time and practice to improve his motor skills before he can get around properly, on his hands and knees. Then there will be no stopping him. He still has plenty to learn, however, and will sit and play quite contentedly if the toys are within his reach.

DIARY 27TH JANUARY

Dean has found his feet, so he writhes around trying to hold onto them. I'm sure he'd try and get them into his mouth if he could. It is becoming very difficult to put his nappy on now as he looks at his feet and tries to play with them.

He can sit – he's getting much better at that. If he starts to fall to one side he puts his hand there and balances himself.

He's teething badly at the moment, dribbling a lot and gnawing at everything. He sucks his thumb, he sticks his fists in his mouth – anything he can grab hold of he sticks in his mouth.

PLAYTIME

Playing is not just for fun, though unless it is fun, of course, it becomes boring and more like drudgery. A young baby learns through play: he learns to perfect both his fine and gross motor skills by crawling after a toy, for example, or picking up a very small brick; he learns to 'put two and two together' when he plays; he begins to realize that when he shakes a rattle it makes an interesting sound.

In this way he begins to build up memory and to study elementary cause and effect. He gradually learns to solve problems through play and it helps him come to terms with the permanence of objects. Later on, play helps him learn to share and to socialize and make friends with other people. All in all, play is an essential part of a child's life and not just a luxury. Although learning comes through play; to a child, play is fun.

A baby's first playfellow is usually his mother, the person primarily responsible for care. A mother's early play with her children can involve cuddles and tickles and lots of love and laughs, with opportunities for fun and games available during bathtime, dressing-time and changing-time.

But towards the end of the first month of life, he is ready for his first toy. His dominant sense at this stage is vision, so he will appreciate something to look at – a mobile over his cot, for example – within his rather short visual range. By about three months he is playing with his fingers and his hand-eye coordination is improving. He now needs toys to grasp and touch as he becomes aware of his hands.

Teaching with toys

All toys teach babies something. Different toys have different textures, for example, so he will learn the difference between a hard ball and a soft teddy bear. Toys come in all shapes, sizes and colours, so he will eventually learn about the differences between things as well as the similarities. Reaching for toys helps him perfect his hand-eye coordination and playing with them in his hands improves his fine manipulative skills. Later still he will learn to run, hop and skip as well as how to kick and catch a ball. These are all fairly advanced motor skills which are generated and nurtured by spontaneous play.

Older play

Not all play is necessarily physical, though. Books are marvellous playthings and provide hours of amusement. Interest in books can start well before one year of age, and most children find being read to a great pleasure. Similarly, young children often love to scribble or to make or listen to music.

During the third year, however, the nature of children's play tends to change. As they begin to use their imagination, inventive, make-believe play develops, and children start to devise complex, fantasy situations on which to base their play.

Dean loves playing with his wooden bricks – but it is not just play, even though he seems to enjoy it so much. All the time, he is learning: beginning to understand about colour and texture, and practising his grasping, reaching and manipulative skills, *above*.

He has grasped a brick, *far left*, with both hands; two weeks later he can hold a brick in each hand at the same time, *left*, invariably mouthing each one in turn.

In another game, *right*, Dean resists Annette's gentle tugging as he holds on to the tail of the colourful knitted mouse.

41

CHAPTER THREE

PART OF THE FAMILY

Human beings occupy a unique position in the animal kingdom. Not only can we walk upright and use complicated tools with great manipulative skill, but we also have a highly developed spoken language with which to communicate, and we live in complex cultural groups.

This sophisticated behaviour takes some time to assimilate and learn, which is the reason why it takes such a relatively long time for humans to become sexually mature and independent. And this period of childhood is spent in the basic human social group, the family. Being part of the family confers undoubted advantages. It gives the young human shelter and food, so that he can mature and acquire skills in a safe environment without the need to go out in search for food. Indeed, at birth the human baby is totally helpless and therefore dependent on his mother for everything he needs to survive.

Little by little, however, the young human grows up, learns how to use his hands and how to move about. Soon he can feed himself, though as yet he is unable to fend for himself. He learns to talk and read and write and eventually becomes experienced in the ways of the world. Somewhere between the ages of twelve and eighteeen years, he becomes sexually mature, and later on may set up a family of his own.

He has formed his first relationships within the family, and has been nurtured by his parents up to an age of maturity. If, like Dean, he is lucky, he has had a safe, happy childhood, full of fun and happy memories. He now has a store of knowledge and experience that he will be able to use to protect and bring up his own children.

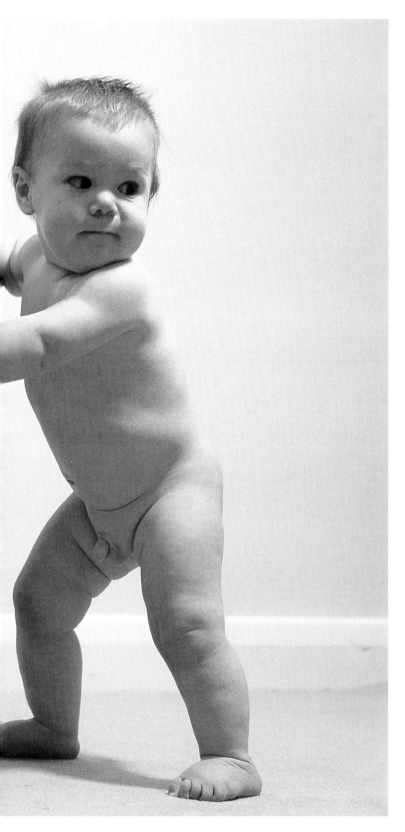

By six months Dean is more mobile and can now support his weight with a little help when placed in a standing position. He is becoming more confident and self-assured, and knows exactly what he wants to do. Although he cannot yet talk he makes a lot of noise and has no difficulty in making his likes and dislikes understood.

HALFWAY HOUSE

Halfway through his first year of life, the new baby has already learned a lot. Physically, he is much bigger and stronger than he was, and has better balance and coordination. He has mastered the major manoeuvres: rolling over from front to back and round the other way as well, and how to sit up.

He can even sit up by himself with a good stable base and straight back – but only for a few moments. He may be able to support his weight crouching on all fours, though he cannot yet crawl. He manages to get around quite well, though, by wriggling and squirming along on his tummy. Moving around like this he seems to be able to cover a good deal of ground and is always getting into mischief. His parents need to keep a close eye on him at all times – not that they would ever be able to forget him for long, because he is very vocal and demands lots of attention.

He likes to be able to see everything and will lift his head and upper chest up off the ground so that he can look around. He enjoys kicking his legs strongly, whether lying on his back or tummy, in preparation for crawling. When held upright on a firm surface he will support his weight on his legs and may bounce up and down on his feet.

He looks at everything with great interest, turning his head around and following movements avidly with his eyes. He will reach out for a small toy and is able to grasp it – usually with both hands and sometimes with his feet. He tends to hold things in the palm of his hands and pass them backwards and forwards from one hand to the other, examining them closely as he does so.

He puts everything in his mouth: toys, fists and even toes. This stage is called 'mouthing' for obvious reasons, and means that all toys should be large enough so that they cannot be swallowed accidentally. He will grasp his rattle and shake it deliberately because he has learned that this is the way to make a sound. He is not yet able to put it down voluntarily, however, so just lets go and watches it drop. If it falls within his visual field he will probably continue to look at it, whereas if it falls outside his visual field he usually forgets about it immediately or searches around for it in a rather vague, half-hearted way.

He makes quite a noise; singing to himself and laughing and squealing. He will also scream when he is fed up, over-tired or bored. Just as he can make his own feelings known, he is beginning to show that he can understand what is meant by the different tones of voice that his mother uses. He is very friendly and loves having a fuss made of him, though he is beginning to be wary of strangers and feels happier when he can see his mother nearby. He knows his own name and turns his head when he is called.

By now he will be eating some solids and may have a tooth or two. He still enjoys being breast-fed at night, however; partly for the opportunity to cuddle up close to his mother after a busy day. He may try and help with feeding by putting his hands around his bottle and will sometimes hold a small rusk. As he is awake for most of the day, he usually sleeps throughout the night; unless he is unwell, of course, and does not want a night-time feed.

Although he knows what happens at mealtimes, bathtime and during dressing, and may well attempt to join in, he is still incapable of looking after himself. At six months old, he continues to need the constant love, care and attention from his parents.

Dean is holding the upper half of his body off the floor on his outstretched arms, *left above*. He is dribbling because some teeth have just come through. Even though he cannot yet crawl, he is adopting the correct position to do so, *left below*, and looks happy, healthy and interested. Even so, he still spends a lot of time sucking his thumb and cuddling his mother, *right*.

DIARY 10TH FEBRUARY

Six months today and Dean moves backwards with great ease now! He gets up on all fours and rocks backwards and forwards, and then rather than push himself forwards, he'll push himself backwards. The other day I left the room for a couple of minutes and then I heard a little squeak, and came back to an empty room. I looked for Dean and discovered that he'd disappeared right underneath the table, so I had to pull him out as he couldn't move forwards.

THE FAMILY WAY

Inevitably, a new baby is closest to his mother at first. Hers is the face that he sees most often, and it is her body that he nestles up to during feeding. The mother is the person who takes most care of him, keeping him warm and wellfed and comforting him whenever necessary. And it is the mother, too, who usually feels closest to the new baby. After all, she is the one who has already lived with the baby for the nine months of pregnancy and her hormonally-governed maternal responses are geared to protect and nurture her offspring.

But this does not mean to say that all mothers fall head over heels in love with their new babies. Indeed, many women find it difficult to adore their small, screaming, demanding little babies who take so much at first and seem to give so little. The very helplessness and dependence that appeals to one woman may be rather frightening and off-putting to another. Proper emotional bonding, which forms the basis of a lifelong loving relationship, may take months, or even a year, to become firmly established.

Nevertheless, during the first few months of life, the relationship between a mother and her new baby is necessarily one of emotional and physical closeness. It is hardly surprising, then, that other members of the family may feel a bit left out.

The father's role

Fathers are often excluded from the delivery room if there are complications, and in any event sometimes have to rush back to work the next day – regardless of the major new event in their lives. From then on, most fathers have to spend most of their new child's waking day at work. As a result, they hardly ever see their young children, except at weekends.

Fathers might feel further excluded by the process of breast-feeding, which often takes up a great deal of time during the first few weeks. No wonder some fathers feel left out and slightly jealous of a new baby. A child takes up so much of the mother's time and keeps her awake at night so that she is often too tired to enjoy their usual sex life. And babies have an irritating habit of waking up and screaming at precisely the wrong moment.

So fatherhood can be a frustrating business. At first, a father normally has to accept that he has to take a back seat and look after his child indirectly – by caring for and supporting his partner so that she can devote her time and energy to the new baby.

Later on, though, as the baby grows older, fathers come into their own. They become able to form their own, unique relationships with their children – relationships that are different from maternal ones, but every bit as important as them. They can become wonderful playmates, and teachers, too, showing their children a variety of different skills. Traditionally, such skills are thought to tend towards fishing, football and running a train set, but nowadays fathers enjoy teaching skills that can also include reading, writing and the social arts, and be passed to both sons and daughters alike.

The other children

Older children often find the arrival of a new baby rather threatening. They have been the centre of attention for the past few years and probably find it difficult to accept that a rival is taking up so much of their parents' time. A certain amount of jealousy and

---

DIARY 16TH FEBRUARY

Dean seems to show more interest in Gemma's toys than his rattles; perhaps he thinks they are superior to his. He loves watching Gemma – he gets a lot of pleasure just watching what she is up to. She, on the other hand, doesn't like him touching her and she says, "No, go away." Anything that she's got and he touches, she hates – she tells him off, or smacks him.

His ability to reach out and grab things has improved ten-fold and he is impossible when we have any food around. His appetite is even larger than Gemma's and he gets very jealous if we're eating and he is not.

Jason plays a full part in looking after Dean, *left*, and makes sure that Gemma is not left out. He has to restrain Dean from grabbing at Gemma's biscuit, but Gemma, who is developing social skills of her own, offers her baby brother a bite, *below*.

Dean has started to cry, *left* – maybe he is just hungry, or frustrated by his building blocks – but Gemma is alarmed and looks round for help. Eventually, she takes on the role of comforter, *above*, and puts a protective arm around him – and it seems to work.

resentment is only natural, but it can usually be overcome with the constant reassurance of their parents that they are still loved, and the reminder that they were once helpless babies themselves. There will probably still be tantrums, though, but that is because young children do not fully understand the concepts of sharing and of right and wrong.

For example, if the baby sees something he wants, he grabs it. But if this toy belongs to an older child, she may not want him to have it. A small fight will follow, and the whole thing will probably end in tears. This is all part and parcel of growing up – in fact it is one of the ways in which young children learn to play with each other and share their toys.

As the children grow up together they usually become firm friends and seek out each other's company. They will frequently play together for hours, often creating imaginary situations, with the older child protecting and comforting the younger child, as she has seen her parents do so often.

This is the way that a young baby learns most of his early social skills. He learns about people and his surroundings, and about how to behave within the family group. He has people to play with, people to teach him and people to look after him and comfort him when he is upset.

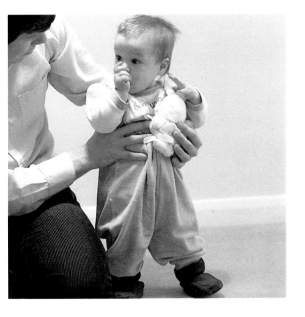

After an afternoon of rough and tumble type play, Dean is tired and a little unsure of himself, *above*. He sucks his thumb for comfort and holds on tightly to the white rabbit, his favourite toy.

Gemma and Dean sitting quietly together at the end of the afternoon, *above*. Dean is sucking his thumb because he is tired, while Gemma is drinking from a feeding mug – she has probably borrowed Dean's, because she has been drinking out of a normal plastic cup for some time.

Among their many other qualities, fathers can be used as indoor climbing frames, making excellent play horses, *left*. Gemma is riding on Jason's back whilst Dean gazes intently at a small toy.

SOLID FOOD

A new baby needs food not only for survival and warmth, but to fuel the enormous amount of growth that takes place in the first year – his weight will generally increase by about seven kilograms (15 lb). He needs a diet of carbohydrate, fat, protein, minerals and vitamins to ensure healthy growth and development.

Initially, all his nutritional requirements are supplied by milk, which can come from various sources. Breast milk has everything he needs in exactly the right proportions and at the correct temperature. Formula feeds, used when a baby is bottle-fed, are made from cows' milk that has been modified until it closely resembles human milk. Modified soya milk is also available for those few babies that are allergic to cows' milk.

Whatever type of milk is chosen, it forms the baby's staple diet for the first few months of life. Although it sounds rather dreary and boring to an adult palate, and would certainly fail to please an older child, babies know no other than their milk diet and they thrive on it.

The first mouthful

After several months of a liquid diet, solid food is certainly different. It feels different, tastes different and comes on an inedible spoon. It all adds up to an exciting new experience for a baby.

There are two reasons why solids are necessary at this stage of growth. First, the growing baby now needs so many calories that he would have to drink a huge volume of milk at each feed if milk alone was the sole source of those calories: this would simply be impractical. Second, the baby has now reached the

His eyes alight with excitement and anticipation, Dean reaches for a small rusk. He loves his food and cannot wait to put the rusk in his mouth, even though he only has a few bottom teeth with which to chew it.

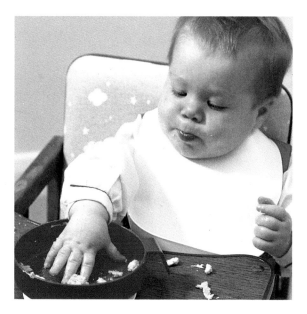

Like most babies, Dean prizes effectiveness above elegance
when it comes to feeding time, scooping up whole handfuls
of food and stuffing them into his mouth, *right*. Sensibly,
Annette has given Dean a stiff plastic bib to catch the
spillage, has sat him in a washable high-chair, and given
him an unbreakable red bowl that has a firm base so that it
does not tip over or move around, *above*.

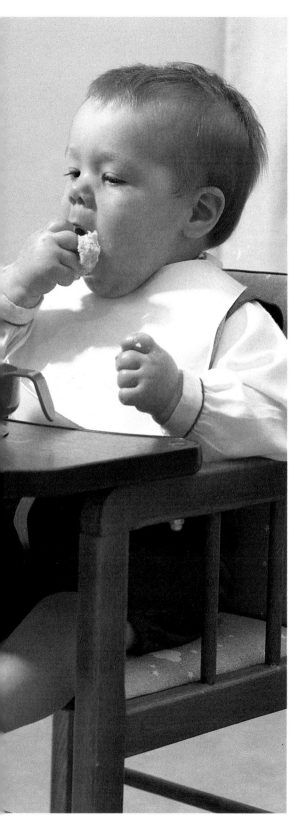

stage at which he needs to chew rather than suck, so that the jaw, the teeth and the muscles used in chewing can develop properly. And in order to encourage this growth, he needs solid foods on which he can chew.

The process by which solids are introduced into the diet while the amount of milk is reduced is called weaning. The word comes from the old English term *wenian*, meaning 'accustom'. And this is absolutely appropriate. Little by little, the baby becomes accustomed to his new diet.

In fact, the first solids are not really very solid at all. They are fine purées of fruit, vegetables or cereals

Dean has managed to throw his bowl onto the floor and is now looking to see where it has gone, *above*. He was sensible enough to empty it beforehand, though.

mixed with milk to make them easy to swallow. Initially, about half to one teaspoon of the chosen solid is offered before one of the daytime milk feeds.

Don't worry if the baby does not like the taste of his new food and spits it out. At this stage of weaning he is still getting all his nourishment from milk and the first few spoonfuls are really only intended to introduce him to a different texture and flavour.

After a couple of days of one particular food, or if the baby doesn't like the food he has been offered, try another one. Even at this age, babies have definite preferences and make it quite clear which tastes they like and dislike. At this stage it is important to avoid

Gemma and Dean having a sociable drink together, *above*. Unlike Gemma, Dean cannot yet handle a plastic beaker, and has to use a plastic feeding cup with a lid.

battles over food, so do not force them to eat something they are not keen to try.

Babies generally like sweet tastes, though, and may prefer fruit purées to cereals unless the latter have been sweetened. Some mothers like to buy specially prepared tinned or packet baby food while others prefer to purée adult food for the baby. Tinned baby food is very convenient and nourishing, but giving the baby the same food as the rest of the family does have distinct advantages. After all, he will soon be on a full mixed diet and eventually eat with the rest of the family so it can be a good idea to get him used to family food from the start.

Mealtimes
Mealtimes are family affairs. Once the baby is weaned, he can sit at the table in his high chair. He will have to be spoon-fed at first, but by seven months he will start trying to grab the spoon to feed himself, and to drink from a two-handled cup.

At first, his hand-to-eye coordination is not very good, and large amounts of food finish up all over his face or spilled down his front. But practise makes perfect, and picking up a finger of toast and putting it in his mouth helps him to improve his coordination and manipulative skills.

Food is fun and a baby generally loves it. He enjoys the different colours, shapes, tastes and textures and this helps him to learn about the differences between various foods. He will already have a number of teeth, though there are still some coming through, and chewing on a piece of apple or carrot is just what he needs to help them. But he should never be left alone, of course, in case he chokes.

Dean enjoys a drink after his midday meal, *above*. Even though his feeding cup has a lid, he has still managed to splash his drink all over the place. Luckily his bib has caught the worst of it. But even after he has eaten and drunk everything, he still wants more and cries for Annette, *right*.

DIARY 18TH MARCH

Last week Dean grabbed hold of Gemma's cup and drank the contents and so now we encourage him to drink from a cup placed in front of him. The cup has handles so he can grab hold of either one and tip it up, although he makes himself very wet in the process. He is much better at feeding himself; I give him bread and butter and his brain is now functioning quite quickly, 'hand to bread, bread to mouth'; mind you everything eventually goes into his mouth.

55

TEETHING

Around one baby in 1,200 is born with a tooth, but the majority of babies do not cut their first tooth until they are about five or six months. Usually a front tooth, or incisor, is the first to appear, on the bottom jaw. A few weeks later, the one next to it starts to emerge. Teething often causes discomfort, but is rarely the cause of actual illness, so if a teething baby becomes unwell you should call or see a doctor straight away.

In fact, babies start to chew months before they have their first cutting or chewing teeth, trying to gnaw at hands and toys as soon as they can put them into their mouths. They have a need to chew, and because their first solid food is, in fact, quite sloppy, it is a good idea to give them something additional to chew on – a slice of apple, for example.

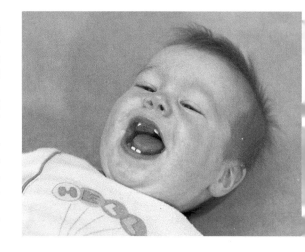

DIARY 26TH MARCH

After much trouble teething, Dean's first two teeth surfaced on the same day – the 27th of January. He'd been gnawing at everything so hopefully this gave him some relief.

Now he's got four teeth and they have not come through in the order that is normally expected – he has two at the bottom and two fangs at the top which are either side of the front two teeth. He is trying to cut the front two now so we're going through it all again – moans and runny nappies, dribbling and being fractious.

At five months, Dean is just about to start teething, *above left*, and by twenty-six weeks he is happy to show off two brand new teeth, *far right*. Both are cutting, rather than chewing, teeth, and, as is usual, are in the middle of the lower jaw. By thirty-eight weeks, *top*, Dean is the proud possessor of four teeth. Here, two are in the upper jaw and two in the lower, though sometimes the four teeth emerge to form a line in the lower jaw. At ten months old, Dean has six teeth; two more have come through in the upper jaw, *above*.

TOOTH CARE
● Never give a baby a dummy that has been filled with or dipped into, sweet fruit syrup. This may keep the baby quiet, but leads to tooth decay.
● Make sure the baby's diet is rich in foods that contain calcium and vitamin D. Both are essential for strong, healthy teeth.
● Brush the baby's teeth regularly with a soft brush – this is especially important after the first year, when the molars have appeared – and visit the dentist every so often for a check-up.

THE INQUIRING MIND

During the first year of life, the new baby does not just grow in a physical sense, but is also developing his mental powers. At birth he is equipped with the same senses as an adult, but has neither the memory nor the reasoning power to make the most of them. This does not mean that he has no idea what is going on at all; just that he has no past experience stored away in his memory to interpret what is happening, nor can he anticipate what may happen in the future. He can smell and touch but cannot as yet process the information fully, so is unlikely to understand the significance of what he perceives.

For example, a baby sees a transistor radio as a small dark box, but does not know that it can produce sound when switched on. An older child knows what a radio does and is usually capable of turning it on to produce the sound when required. The perceptual world of the new baby is also limited to his immediate vicinity, as, unlike an older child, he cannot move about to search for things, neither can he read nor understand the radio or TV.

As the baby grows older, he gradually stores away the information he has gathered and builds up a body of experience. He begins to recognize the similarities between things so that he can assign them to certain groups, and also starts to appreciate the differences between objects. In order to do this, of course, he has to see lots of things for himself and notice that they are not all the same. This is why young children are so inquisitive, ask so many questions and explore the outside world so avidly. Most of the things that adults take for granted are new and exciting to children, who need to understand them and learn about them so that they can accumulate a fund of knowledge and experience for future use.

Piaget

Psychologists have watched very young babies and children under experimental conditions and have drawn many conclusions about the way they think. Probably the most famous of these scientists has been Piaget, a Swiss psychologist who pioneered much of the work in this field and wrote extensively on it. Over the years, though, many of his ideas have been challenged, and it now seems that a number of his conclusions may have been incorrect.

One of the mainstays of Piaget's theories is that the young child is extremely limited in his abilities to think and reason. This is said to be because the young child is self-obsessed and quite unable to understand

Dean, looking in a mirror, *left*, seems to know that he is not looking at a real person because he has reached out and touched the mirror glass. But does he realize that he is looking at a reflection of himself, or does he think it is a picture of another small boy? It is difficult to know exactly what he is thinking, but, by a year a baby's self-image is generally so good that he can recognize himself in the mirror. Dean already knows, however, that if he picks up a bell and shakes it, *above*, it will make a noise. He enjoys being able to produce a noise when he chooses, and the bell has become a favourite toy.

DIARY 7TH APRIL

I noticed, a little while ago, Dean's reaction to himself in the mirror. He has a mirror beside his changing mat in his bedroom and he was fascinated by the reflection he was seeing as if he thought it was another baby – he started to interact with it, smiling and patting it, and he did that today, looking at it and talking to himself. He hates to be left alone in a room by himself, even surrounded by toys, he likes to hear noise rather than silence, and he likes to see someone, even if it's only Gemma playing around.

other points of view, only coming to see things differently around the age of seven.

Very few people would now agree that the pre-school child is so limited in his understanding, and other psychologists have performed experiments that throw considerable doubt on some of Piaget's theories.

In particular, there is dispute about Piaget's belief in the profound egocentricity of a young baby, unable to distinguish between himself and the rest of the world and unconscious of anything outside himself. In Piaget's theory an object only exists for a baby when he can see it. If it falls outside his field of vision, the theory goes, or is covered up by something else, it ceases to exist for the baby.

So, if a baby of about four months is playing with a toy, and that toy is covered up with a cloth while the baby is watching, the baby will not attempt to search for it. At about nine months, however, the older baby will actively look for the toy that has been lost or concealed.

It is not that anyone disputes that this is how babies actually behave; rather that people question the reasons for this behaviour.

Opposing theories

Other researchers have since approached the problem in another way: they made the object disappear by turning off all the lights so that the room was in darkness. In this case, young babies reach out in the direction of the vanished toy. If it has ceased to exist for them because they could no longer see it, why did they reach out in the right direction? The answer seems to be that a young baby does not search for a covered toy because he has difficulty in understanding spatial relationships and the concept that things can move, not that he no longer believes it exists.

Theories apart, it is fascinating to watch a young baby explore his world and gradually learn how things work – whether or not he believes in their existence when he cannot see them. Over the months and years to come he will learn how to sort things into groups and how to make comparisons between them. He will begin to understand why things happen and, most important of all, he will begin to learn language, so that he can communicate fluently with his fellow human beings.

Annette has built a tower of eight wooden bricks. After studying them for a while, Dean reaches out a hand to knock the tower over, *right*. It is a good game and he wants to play it all over again, *above*, but Annette is tired of building things that just get knocked over, so has suggested to Dean that he might like to play by himself for a while. By fifteen months, Dean should be able to build his own tower of two bricks (though some babies may do this as early as nine months), and by two years he will probably be able to build a tower six or seven bricks high.

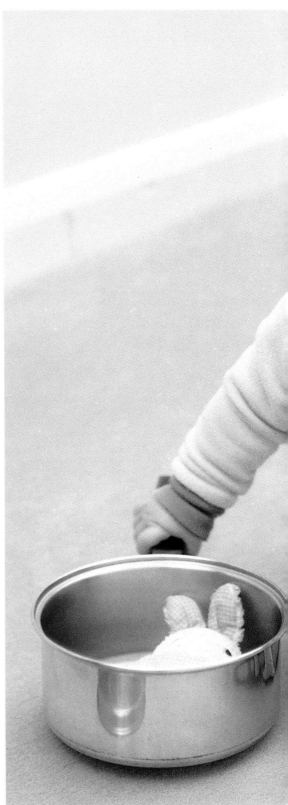

Dean has been playing with Rabbit, one of his favourite toys. Annette put Rabbit in the saucepan, while Dean watched, and put the lid on. As soon as she had finished, Dean went to the saucepan, *above left*, took off the lid, *below left*, and found his toy, *left*. A much younger baby could not have done this – he would have lost interest in the toy as soon as it disappeared from sight.

Dean pulling himself up to a standing position using the sofa for support, *below*. Getting back down again onto all fours, *bottom*, is also carried out carefully, stage by stage. He is still very wobbly at this age and needs to keep holding onto something firm for support. He will side-step or edge along from one piece of furniture to another.

DIARY 7TH APRIL

Dean has mastered the art of crawling. When he's not tired he can seem to do it in a flash; when he's a bit tired he goes slower, and eventually just lies flat on his tummy and sucks his thumb. If he wants something, he makes his way to it and in fact now he's able to get up onto things by pulling himself up.

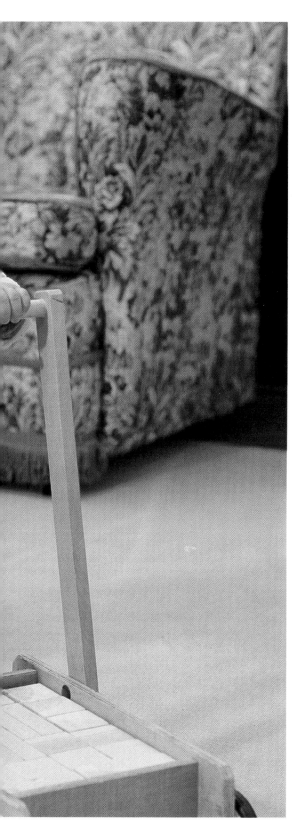

GETTING AROUND

By about nine months, a baby is desperate to explore his surroundings, one way or another. He may be able to crawl at this stage, though this is not always the case, or he may move about by rolling and squirming along the floor instead. He likes to pull himself up into a standing position using the furniture for support, and can stand like this, holding on, for several minutes. He cannot lower himself to the floor successfully, though, so he tends to fall back with a bump. This rarely deters him, and he will pull himself up again and try to move along by holding onto the furniture. This process is known as cruising.

A nine-month baby is not constantly on the move, however. He will sit on the floor for fifteen minutes or so, happily playing with his toys. He can lean over to pick up a fallen toy without losing his balance, and can swivel the top half of his body to look around him. All in all, he is becoming stronger and more coordinated by the day, and it won't be long before he takes his first, tentative steps.

Dean taking his first few steps with the help of a baby walker, *left*. This is a solid, stable wooden cart that does not tip over when he pulls himself up by grabbing the handle. It can be wheeled around safely and provides much-needed support. Nevertheless, even taking steps with support is a demanding business, and Dean has a look of intense concentration on his face, *below*.

CHAPTER FOUR

OUT AND ABOUT

Between seven and nine months, most babies start to crawl. Immediately, a whole new world opens up for them. The new skill means that a baby no longer has to stay put in one spot, but can crawl off on voyages of discovery whenever he pleases. He can crawl towards a toy he wants, or move away from something in which he has lost interest. He can now control where he goes – within the limits set by his parents, of course.

And move about he certainly will. It is amazing how fast babies can crawl. One minute they are where you left them; the next they are getting into mischief somewhere else. It is understandable, because this is the age at which inquisitiveness is at its height. For this reason, too, babies now need a great deal of stimulation; they quickly become bored with familiar things. This does not mean that they need complicated, expensive toys; they will play just as happily with an assortment of cardboard boxes. What they do need is lots of attention and variety. They have to be involved in everything: looking, listening, feeling and often chewing anything that they find.

This means that parents have to be extra careful about the house. Kitchen cupboards need special childproof locks, and it is important to fit gates at the top and bottom of the stairs to prevent accidents.

But above all, this is an age for discovery and learning, with new skills being acquired all the time. Babies begin to understand the odd word, start to feed themselves and can distinguish strangers from members of the family. It is a pleasure to watch how they enjoy the process.

Rabbit has long been a favourite toy, and Dean takes it everywhere. Sometimes, though, it is not too easy. Here Dean has solved the tricky problem of how to carry it when both hands are occupied by picking it up in his mouth.

This shows great ingenuity and concentration, especially as Dean has not been crawling for very long. How did he work it out? Had he seen a cat carrying something this way, or was it instinct?

THE FIRST WAVE

After nine months of learning and experience, a baby has grown and developed into a lively, responsive young child with a mind of his own. This becomes apparent through his developing skills in communication, which allow a sense of his character to shine through.

He can make himself understood, for example, even though he cannot speak properly, and there are no doubts about his likes and dislikes. He is not silent, however – far from it. He babbles continually, making lots of different noises to express himself, and seems to imitate speech. In fact, by nine months babies can often say a couple of words: usually 'dada' and 'mama'. What is more, they know what these words mean. They also understand the meaning of 'no' and 'bye-bye', and have come to associate the latter with people waving. It is a short step from this association for babies to start waving themselves when someone says 'bye-bye'.

Social behaviour

Now that a baby is beginning to learn a means of communication – both verbal and non-verbal – he becomes able to express his developing social skills. He is very responsive to familiar adults and makes it clear that he enjoys playing imitative games with them – peek-a-boo, or pat-a-cake, for example. And although he quickly becomes bored with the same old game, he is also starting to show signs of persistence, continuing to do something and refusing to be distracted when it suits him.

Not any adult will do, though. He is not as fond of strangers, and is much more clingy with his mother than he used to be. He likes to play near her and may become rather upset and edgy if his mother suddenly leaves him alone. This is not because he lacks confidence generally; rather it is because as a growing baby he is becoming more discriminating – he now knows who he is, who his mother is and who he likes to seek approval from.

This growing sense of discrimination and awareness makes a baby even more of a delight to his parents. He has always been an individual, of course – right from the start. But now, as he becomes able to express himself by one means or another, his own personality becomes more apparent; he is revealing personal thoughts and responses: in fact, a character.

Ever-ready to learn, Dean stares intently into the water of the garden pond, *above*. But he is not just learning about pond life – Annette constantly talks to him, explaining what is going on, and it is through this that he develops his skills in communication. Imitation, too, is important – Dean has learned to wave 'bye-bye', *right*, by watching other people and learning from them – even if he is sometimes sorry to see them go.

Dean is not crawling properly outside yet, but this does not seem to stop him getting around the garden. In fact, he is growing more and more confident each day, and Annette has to keep a close eye on him to make sure he is not about to cause himself injury or harm.

Here Dean is taking his weight on his hands while he kicks his legs in the air – a head-down, bottom-up position that is typical of babies who are on the point of crawling. Soon, he will be able to support himself evenly on his hands and knees, and propel himself forward.

COMPETITION

The arrival of a new baby can be a worrying and unsettling time for a young child. From being the only child in a family, used to receiving all the attention, an older child has to accept the presence of a new, and more defenceless brother or sister, who takes up a lot of mother's and father's time.

Not surprisingly, the adjustment can be a difficult one for some children to make. On the one hand they are excited about the new baby and all the preparations this entails. On the other they are frightened that the new baby will take up all their parents' time, attention and affection, making them feel left out and lonely.

It is important that parents are aware of these feelings and are able to deal with them sensitively. Older brothers or sisters have to understand that he or she is still very much loved, and that nothing can or will alter that fact. They have to find out that there is plenty of love to go round; that parents' love is not rationed and that the new baby is not stealing anything that is theirs. Instead, he is adding to the total amount of love in the family: they will eventually learn to love him and he will love them in return.

Inevitably there will obviously be some jealousy, though, with a few tantrums and squabbles. The baby will not understand about sharing at first, and this is likely to cause trouble when, perhaps, he takes a toy that belongs to an older child.

A tug-of-war or even a small fight which ends in tears may be the result. But this does not usually last long, and is of no major significance. Within minutes both children will have forgotten the argument and be playing together happily.

Small boys have a way of demanding attention, *far right*. Annette has just sat down hoping for a moment's peace and quiet but Dean is quick to make his presence felt. But Gemma likes playing with Dean, too – especially when his nose can be tickled when he is flat on his back, *right*. Dean does not approve, and starts to scream for help.

Even big girls need a cuddle from Mummy sometimes, *left*. Here Annette shows Gemma that she is still loved despite all the time and attention demanded by Dean, who is snuggling in her lap.

DIARY 28TH APRIL

Socially, Dean is learning to fight his own battles; if Gemma has a toy that he wants he will now make a noise and scream if she actually takes it back from him, and if she's close enough he'll go for her hair and then of course Gemma screams.

    He's also now, in his own way, showing the direction in which he wants to go; if you want him to do something and you take his toy away from him he will scream and clench his fists, and if he's hungry he will go to his highchair. He is now making the world do what he wants.

CRAWLING

Though not yet able to stand or walk unaided, an older baby can move around safely and swiftly by crawling on all fours. Now he can choose where to go and no longer has to stay where he was put. And crawling is a remarkably efficient way of moving around, as any parent who has watched their baby slither off at an alarming rate will testify.

The age at which babies learn to crawl varies between about seven months and one year. Indeed, some babies never crawl in the true sense, but progress directly from shuffling around on their bottoms to cruising around the furniture. Other babies creep on their hands and feet like little bears, rather than crawling on their hands and knees.

Usually however, a baby's neuro-muscular power, coordination and sense of balance will have become sufficiently developed to allow him to start to crawl at nine months. He will have been preparing to crawl for some time before this – ever since he sat up independently, in fact. For several months he will have been pushing himself up on all fours, but been unable to move off forwards.

By nine months, then, he can be ready to go. But unfortunately he does not always go in the right direction. Many babies start by crawling backwards – it must be very frustrating indeed. Eventually, however, he manages to move off forwards, and from then on there is no stopping him.

He is now truly mobile for the first time in his life, and makes full use of his new skill, following his mother around and exploring everything. He may get underfoot occasionally, and will certainly get his hands and knees dirty, but no matter: he is having fun and learning all the time.

STARTING TO CRAWL

● Not all babies crawl at the same age. Some start as early as seven months, while others do not crawl until eleven months or so. This is perfectly normal. Your baby will begin to crawl when the time is right for him, not when a textbook says he should.

● Some babies miss out crawling altogether and go directly from bottom shuffling to cruising around the furniture and then walking independently.

● Babies who do crawl often move about very quickly indeed. It only takes a few seconds for them to get to the unguarded fire or a hot cup of tea on a low table.

● Be sure to make the house safe for the crawling baby: guard all fires; cover electric power points so that little fingers cannot pry; fit childproof locks on kitchen cupboards; keep all medicines and harmful substances in safe places where they cannot be found and eaten accidentally; put a gate at the top and bottom of the stairs; and make sure the kitchen is safe and that a saucepan or kettle cannot be pulled over.

● All dangerous objects like scissors, knives and matches should always be kept out of sight and reach until he is old enough to learn how to use them safely.

● Once the house is safe for the baby, let him have the freedom to crawl around and play as he wants: he will become frustrated if he is cooped up all day. Nevertheless, you cannot foresee every possible danger, so keep a close eye on him at all times.

● When travelling in a car, make sure he is strapped into a car seat that meets with safety regulations and never leave him unattended in the car.

Crawling is difficult to learn, but once learnt can get a baby around very quickly indeed. Here Dean is on all fours with his weight distributed evenly between his hands and knees. First, he reaches forward with his left arm and advances his right knee, *near right*. Then he reaches with the other arm and brings up his left knee, pushing with his knees and pulling with his arms so that his whole body moves, *centre right*. Then he stops, lifting his feet and looking very pleased with himself, *far right*.

Dean crawling along with a bowl in his right hand, *below* – a more complicated business than straightforward crawling. In fact, it usually takes another full month for babies to learn to do this after they have started to crawl.

VISION

The ability to see is important for normal physical and mental development during the first year of life. Babies with impaired sight find it very difficult to reach for objects, for example, and also to take independent steps. But these differences are rarely apparent during the first few weeks of life, and so it is very difficult to assess whether a young baby can, in fact, see properly. Curiously, both blind and sighted babies behave in the same way at first. Both stare at their hands, for example, even though the blind baby will be unable to see them.

So, because a very young baby cannot read letters on a sight-testing card held in front of him, other tests have been devised to screen babies and small children for visual problems.

The seeing eye
A newborn baby will blink at a bright light and will turn towards the source of more diffuse light. By about a month old, he will fix his gaze on a small ball held about twenty-five centimetres (10 in) in front of his face, and will follow it with his eyes when it is moved within his visual field. At this age he seems intent on watching his mother's face, and prefers examining a human face to anything else.

By three months, a baby's visual alertness has increased considerably. He gazes around, follows his mother's movements with his eyes and looks at his hands, clasping and unclasping them in front of his face. Over the next few months he continues to watch everything going on around him with great interest. By about six months he is able to fix his eyes on a toy held about twenty-three centimetres (9 in) away from his face, and reach out his hands at the same time to grab it. He pays close attention to objects and inspects them carefully, turning them upside down to get a closer look.

By nine months he is even more alert and interested. He can poke at things with his index finger and pick up a grape or small object between his finger and thumb in a pincer grasp, and so he can obviously see the things he is manipulating. He also shows an interest in what is going on in the near distance, very obviously watching and following a very small ball, about thirty millimetres (⅛ in) in diameter, being rolled across the room three metres (10ft) away. By one year he will be able to scribble on a piece of paper with a crayon, and probably be interested in looking at brightly coloured pictures. He may also enjoy standing at the window watching people walking past, and will often point out what is happening.

Later on, at about two years, he should be able to match the shape of letters. At a routine check-up an examiner will hold up a card with a letter on it, and the young child will be asked to point to a similar shape on another card.

Mothers are usually the first to suspect that their baby cannot see very well, and any mother who is worried should seek medical advice. Experience and patience in testing are vital, because a young child can easily become distracted, tired or fed up.

Any problems are usually picked up at a routine developmental screening, of which sight-testing is an essential part – essential because the sooner poor vision, squints and other visual defects are detected, the sooner a child can be treated so that his overall development is not affected too much.

DIARY 8TH MAY

Dean is showing a lot of interest in sounds, the way different things make different noises. He enjoys banging on cupboards, and today he found the potty and he was just banging it backwards and forwards and pushing it against other surfaces, delighting in the sound he was making. He found the pedal bin, and he was fascinated because it is stainless steel and he could see a slight reflection. He also makes his way to the top of the steps, looks down, and, of course, he has no concept of height and depth so we have to watch him or he might throw himself down.

There is no doubt that Dean can see a small red ball rolled across the carpet about three metres (10ft) away, *right*. In fact, at nine months, babies can see and follow a whole series of small balls, with diameters ranging from five centimetres (2 in) down to thirty millimetres (⅛ in) when they are rolled in front of them at this distance. But a baby has to be in the right mood to perform the test, with nothing to distract him.

COPING WITH TWO

Babies are tremendous fun, there is no doubt about it. But looking after them tends to be a full-time job, and the sudden loss of independence and freedom affects some mothers badly, however much they love their babies. It can be both better and worse the second time round. On the one hand, the second pregnancy is less frightening as everything is more familiar, and looking after a new baby is much less daunting. On the other hand, it is extremely difficult to find any time to rest when there is also a toddler to look after and entertain.

After the birth, time has to be shared between the two children, rather than devoted to the new baby as it was the first time. A simple trip to the shops can seem like a military exercise: both children have to be dressed in their outdoor clothes, then one put in a buggy and the other held by the hand – unless, of course, the older one wants to take the tricycle as well. It seems daunting at first, but most mothers soon learn how to cope.

Eventually, though, life settles down a bit and there is time to sit back and enjoy the sheer pleasure of watching them play together; of seeing the older child take care of the younger and teach him things, and the fascinating way in which the relationship between them develops.

Annette has her hands full, *left*, with Dean, and, of course, Rabbit, on one hip, and Gemma on the other. Mothers soon become adept at doing two things at once, *above*: swinging Dean with one hand and holding Gemma with the other.

Dean having a lovely time in his baby swing, *right*. His infectious grin clearly shows six teeth: two at the bottom and four in a row at the top.

PLAYING OUTSIDE

The outside world provides ample opportunity for further discovery. During fine weather, children can play happily in a garden for hours, providing that it has been made safe. This means locking away garden tools and chemicals, as well as making sure that dangerous areas are fenced off and childproof.

Earth is fun!

The garden provides an interesting contrast to life indoors. There are new textures to discover, from cool, springy grass to sharp, rough gravel. Then, to the dismay of some parents, there is earth. To children, earth is fun. It is rich and brown and contains many interesting things.

Young children have been known to eat earth, and even earthworms. Thankfully, they grow out of this stage quickly, and rarely do themselves any serious harm. But gardens and hedgerows sometimes contain brightly coloured poisonous berries, so it is important to teach older babies and young children not to eat things they might find in the garden.

Playing outside can promote a sense of adventure, too, especially when there are frames to climb and dens to be made. Of course there will be the odd fall and grazed knee, then a splinter or even a wasp sting, but these things can usually be soothed and healed easily; they are not the end of the world and are soon forgotten. Both the baby and his clothes can be washed clean at the end of the day, so there is no need to worry about any mess. Young children enjoy climbing, swinging and sliding. If the garden is big enough then a climbing frame will give them an enormous amount of pleasure, and also help them learn how to climb and balance.

Safety first

A garden can be a magical place for a young child and one in which he will continue his mental and physical development. But it is vital that the garden is made safe for children, preferably without restricting their freedom too much. One particular risk comes from *Toxacara canis*, roundworm larvae found in the excrement of infected dogs, which can – though it is very rare – cause blindness in children. So family dogs should be wormed regularly and the garden kept clear of their excrement.

A collection of large, solid logs, *above*, makes a good, cheap and safe play area for children – though there is always the risk of a splinter. They are arranged in steps to encourage climbing, and are solid enough so that they cannot be toppled over, as Dean is finding while pulling himself up to a standing position.

Crawling across the grass Dean encounters the different texture of the gravel path. It does not deter him though and he is determined to cross. He straightens his legs to protect his knees from the rough surface. A little later, he is making an unusual amount of fuss when Annette changes his nappy, *left*.

THINKING FOR HIMSELF

Between nine months and a year, it gradually becomes obvious to his parents that a baby is beginning to understand what is going on around him. He speaks his first few words – usually 'Mama' and 'Dada', and can also understand a good deal of what his mother says, not just by judging her tone of voice but by recognizing some of the words themselves. He can understand simple commands such as 'wave bye-bye' and 'give it to me', for example, and will usually do as requested; he definitely understands the meaning of 'no'.

Babies develop their short-term memories and learn by watching and listening to parents and older brothers and sisters as they go about their normal routine. They are already beginning to store away knowledge, and can usually point to their noses and may be able to identify other parts of their bodies as well. And babies make it obvious that they are very pleased with themselves when they get things right and are praised.

Physically, a baby at this stage can crawl and stand with support and cruise around the furniture, so that he is forever exploring things and getting into mischief. He is beginning to use one hand in preference to the other, and so is likely to hold an object still with his least-favoured hand while he tries to manipulate it with the other, or best, hand.

Negativism

With this increase in understanding and knowledge comes a clear sense of likes and dislikes, made obvious by both the baby's words, or noises, and facial expression. He is aware of his parents approval or disapproval, and is becoming more affectionate, enjoying being near his mother, but more reserved with strangers.

Towards the end of the first year, he may become less cooperative; refusing food, for example. Some researchers call this the beginning of a period of negativism, which continues into the next year. It sounds rather worrying, but, in fact, it is a sign that the baby is beginning to think for himself and make up his own mind: a necessary and important stage in his development of personality and character.

Until this point, decisions such as when he should eat or what he should wear, have been made by his parents or other adults who have been in charge of

Dean probably realizes that the green wriggly snake has some purpose, *left*, but what is it? Perhaps last time he saw it water was coming out of the end, and he is trying to work out where it has gone. It is all part of his developing understanding of the world around him, as is his expression of likes and dislikes. One thing he certainly likes is playing in the sandpit, *above*, even though he becomes frustrated when the sand will not stay in the container.

DIARY 8TH MAY

I said 'no' to him quite sternly today to see what his reaction was when he was doing something that he shouldn't, and he just smiled. Whether he was just going to ignore me or he actually understood, we'll have to wait and see.

We have a sandpit in the back garden which Dean has discovered; he thinks it's strange but hasn't shown a dislike to it. The sand doesn't taste very nice but it hasn't prevented him from sampling it over and over again. We've also given him a taste of going down the slide and even when I hold him he's not exactly happy. I don't think he's too sure about the height – he's alright coming down but if I just sit him at the top and he looks down, it just scares him.

him. Previously, he was unable to express a prefer-ence about such matters. Now he is able to make his feelings known and understood. Of course, a baby's likes and dislikes may not always fit in with those of his parents, and the result, inevitably, will be a minor disagreement.

Gradually, barely perceptibly, babies begin to become less helpless – in fact, less baby-like – from nine months. They begin to stop taking everything to their mouths, for example, until by a year this is almost uncommon. And they begin to help with feeding, holding their feeding cups by themselves and trying to use a spoon – though not very successfully at first. Fingers are easier, however, and dexterity with a spoon soon follows. Babies also start to help with dressing by holding out their arms and legs to allow clothes to be put on.

A baby enjoys playing imitative games, such as peek-a-boo or clapping-hands-together, at this age, and may be able to hold a coloured crayon and scribble on a piece of paper once he has been shown how to do it. Other favourite games include finding a toy that has been hidden under a box while he watched, and taking little toys in and out of containers. In a group, he will tend to play on his own, alongside other children, rather than actually interacting with them.

Personality

All this adds up to the development of personality. It is a lovely age, when the baby really becomes a person in his own right. He is more aware, more responsive and more affectionate, and looking after him becomes much more rewarding because he is

now such good company. His world is expanding, and, at the same time, he is beginning to understand that other people have likes and dislikes of their own – and, of course, have limits to their patience.

LEARNING THROUGH PLAY

Between nine and twelve months, babies love to explore and discover things. It can be a pleasure for both parents and child. Here are some suggestions:
● Give him a small hand-bell to hold and watch him turn it this way and that, possibly put it in his mouth, and then shake it to make a noise.
● Get him play with a set of brightly coloured wooden bricks. Watch how he picks one up in each hand and then brings his two hands together in front of him, matching one with another.
● Make a very small tower of two or three bricks. He may be able to copy you and build his own tower of two bricks. Then build a much higher tower of several bricks and watch him knock it down time and time again.
● Give him a small, safe, plastic-framed baby mirror to play with. Watch him look at his own reflection.
● Show him how to scribble on a large piece of paper, making sure that the crayons are non-toxic.
● Give him some plasticine or play-dough and let him feel how pliable it is.
● Let him look at bright pictures in a book. See his interest and how he attempts to turn the pages.
● Let him see while you hide a small brick under a beaker and watch him find it.
● Roll a small ball across the carpet about three metres (10ft) from him. Watch how he follows it.

Dean cannot wait to get into the paddling pool, *right*, and has crawled over to it before Annette has had a chance to put his trunks on. The water tastes nice and makes a pleasing sploshing sound.

Annette, Dean and Gemma playing a game of clapping, *above*. Dean loves to imitate his mother and older sister and looks very pleased when he gets it right. In fact, Dean enjoys the paddling pool so much that he has to be persuaded to come out for tea, *left*.

A SWIMMING LESSON

Older babies love expeditions. They are extremely inquisitive and become bored easily. One way to break up the routine is to take them swimming. Some babies love swimming, especially if the water is well-heated and a special time is set aside for baby classes so that the pool is not too noisy and crowded. It is vital that you equip your baby with some flotation aids. A small, inflatable ring that fits round the body snugly and cannot slip off, and inflatable water wings, are ideal. Even properly equipped, a baby needs a close eye kept on him at all times.

Many babies seem to have an instinctive like for water, and are quite fearless in the water; to them all the splashing about is great fun and they enjoy their trip to the swimming pool enormously. But other babies simply cannot stand water: they loathe being bathed and hate having their hair washed, and bathtimes can be a misery for both parents and child.

There is no point at all in forcing such babies to go swimming, indeed it would be cruel to do so. Instead, concentrate on ways of making bathing more pleasurable and, in doing so, taking away their fear of water. With perseverance, they will eventually accept the water, then come to enjoy it. While it is obviously a good idea for a child to learn to swim at an early age, it is never too late to learn.

Dean can get around the pool by doing a type of dog paddle with his legs, *above left*, and he floats easily with the help of his inflatable ring and water wings. Splashing is a great game, *above*, and Dean is only too keen to try it out on any friend who comes near.

Two small children can be quite a handful in a swimming pool, and it is always useful to join other families to help spread the load, *above*. Gemma and Dean enjoy playing with their friends, too, though even Dean eventually reaches the stage where he has had enough, *left*.

Well-protected by his inflatable ring and water wings, and with Annette keeping a close eye on him at all times, Dean is perfectly safe – especially as the pool is reserved for mothers and babies at a certain time each week so that there is less chance of him being frightened by other bigger swimmers or by too much noise.

DIARY 12TH MAY

Dean went swimming for the first time when he was only five months old. He seemed to enjoy it and so today a trip to the pool was greeted with enthusiasm.

Dean finds the booming echoes of noise created by the pool and the other swimmers, a bit off-putting. He definitely prefers to have me an arm's length away. If I move any further away or try to leave him with someone else while I have a swim, he gets very worried. Gemma was never like that. She was always very happy and relaxed in a pool.

Dean likes his water wings and rubber ring as they keep him afloat with his head up and he can kick and splash away quite happily. He was never scared of the water and did not panic about getting into the pool – only if there were lots of other noisy swimmers.

CHAPTER FIVE

WALKING TALL

Towards the end of the first year, a baby's life changes in a most significant way: from living his life mainly in the horizontal plane, he starts to spend most of his time vertical. He may still crawl around for speed and efficiency, but his main interest is in standing upright. This is a milestone in his early life, and one that reflects a vital stage in man's evolutionary progress.

The transition does not take place quickly – in fact it takes many months. Crawling around on all fours requires some skill, but not necessarily a good sense of balance, while standing upright on two very small feet most certainly does. As in the earlier progression – from rolling to sitting to crawling – the transition from being supported on four legs to relying on two happens in stages.

The first stage is for the baby to pull himself up into a vertical position using whatever support is available – usually a solid piece of furniture that will not topple over on top of him. Once upright he learns to move around the room using the furniture for support: side-stepping or cruising along the length of the sofa to the armchair and from there to the sideboard. He can also walk behind a baby-walker or if he is firmly supported by his parents.

Next he has to learn to stand upright without holding on – to really stand alone. The process is fraught with failure, frustration and tears, but he will keep trying – especially with the encouragement of his parents. Eventually he will take his first truly independent step – then watch out! There will be no stopping him.

At just over ten months, Dean can stand upright and take the odd step, but he still needs to hold on to something for balance and support – in this case, Annette's finger. He is totally absorbed in what he is doing and has a look of intense concentration.

DEXTERITY

Human beings are unique for many reasons: they walk upright and have highly developed brains, for example, and a sophisticated language by which they communicate with each other. But there is one other purely human quality, and that is the degree of skill with which they can use their hands for fine manipulation – in a word, dexterity. Human hands can carry out a huge variety of extraordinarily complex tasks: they can hold a pen and write, for example; they can manipulate tools; and, after training, even have the sensitivity to interpret the series of raised dots known as Braille. Human hands are strong, sensitive, supple and adept. Learning to use precision tools such as this obviously takes time. The newborn baby does not really know where his hands are, and keeps his tiny fists clenched shut. At this stage he has a reflex grasp – that is, he will hold a finger placed in the palm of his hand lightly. Over the next couple of months, this reflex grasp disappears, and he starts to unclench his fists as he discovers his fingers and hands. By about three months he hits out at toys and can hold on to a toy that has been placed in his hand with a rather crude, whole-handed grasp. He cannot yet actually pick the toy up with his fingers.

Reaching and grasping

By four months, he is beginning to use his hands more actively. He will reach for nearby toys, grab them and examine them. Over the next couple of months his dexterity improves still further until, at about six months, he is able to reach for a small cube, grasp it in the palm of his hand, manipulate it by rotating his wrist and transfer it from one hand to the other. Soon he can hold a cube in each hand and may be able to bang them together in front of him.

The learning process continues, until at about eight to nine months, he can pick up a small sweet or grape with his thumb and index finger in what is known as a pincer grasp. At the same time, he is

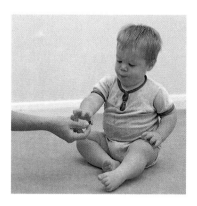

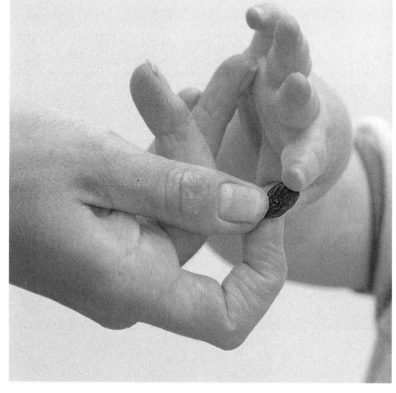

Dean reaches out to take a raisin from Annette, *above*, and then holds it in a pincer grasp between thumb and forefinger, *right*. The ability to use thumb and finger together is unique to humans, and gives us the skill of fine manipulation.

beginning to use his index finger to poke at things, to explore tiny holes, and to point things out.

Later still, he learns how to hold two small objects in the same hand, and also enjoys carrying a toy, or pulling it along on a string. However, although he can pick things up easily enough, he is not so good at putting them down again. At first he simply releases his grasp and the toy falls out of his hand. Towards the end of his first year he starts to put things down deliberately, sometimes banging them down hard on the table. Eventually he learns to put objects down gently and precisely, exactly where he wants them.

Some toys are more likely to encourage a baby to use his hands than others. An assortment of simple wooden building bricks, for example, or a set of small plastic pots that nest one inside one, are ideal and inexpensive. More complicated containers can also be bought, such as those with holes through which smaller shapes' can be posted, or large wooden beads which can be threaded onto a shoe lace.

Dean is having great fun with Annette's hairbrush, *above left*, but is learning manual dexterity at the same time. He is also learning from the brightly coloured toy, *left*, and having hours of amusement while practising his fine motor skills: posting things through the chimney, sliding things up and down the wall, and so on. Even a red plastic tractor, *above*, helps him to learn about wheels and motion while playing.

LANGUAGE

The third specifically human attribute that a baby must learn, after the ability to walk upright and manual dexterity, is the use of language. The various different languages that humans use are extremely sophisticated tools for communication, with vast vocabularies and almost infinite possibilities for exchanging both factual information and abstract thought.

Hearing
The first step towards the understanding of language is to hear it. In fact, babies can hear in the womb, though of course they cannot understand speech. Their ears start to develop towards the end of the first month of fetal life and can function by the fifth month of life inside the womb. Indeed, contrary to popular belief, the womb is a very noisy place.

A baby's hearing ability cannot be accurately tested inside the womb, though, and after the birth it is sometimes difficult to be absolutely certain that a young baby can actually hear. Is he turning towards the sound of his mother's voice, or has he caught sight of her out of the corner of his eye? By the same token, does a baby look startled when a door slams shut because he has heard a loud noise, or because he has just felt a sudden rush of cold air on his face? Deaf babies tend to behave very like babies who can hear, and even make babbling sounds at first.

Even with these difficulties, it is important that any problem with hearing is detected as early as possible, so that the baby can be fitted with a hearing aid and taught special skills. Newborn babies can be tested by means of a special auditory cradle, though this is generally reserved for babies who run a high risk of deafness, such as those born to mothers who had German measles during early pregnancy. Most babies are tested at all their developmental check-ups, but particularly at eight months of age, when a baby can sit by himself and is generally alert and fairly cooperative.

Listening and learning
Just as a baby watches his mother intently, so he will listen to her speech all the time. And as long as parents talk to their babies, they will learn to speak through imitating the sounds.

Long before a baby can say his first word, he has communicated all his needs to his mother by crying. From about six weeks, he starts to make cooing and gurgling noises. Over the next few months his repertoire of sounds increases, so that he chuckles and squeals in delight and by about four months begins to babble. This babbling becomes increasingly more tuneful and controlled as he varies the pitch and volume, imitating the rhythms of speech. Babies whose parents talk to them a lot babble more than others who are less fortunate, possibly because they have older brothers or sisters who also need attention, or because they are one of a pair of twins, so only get half the usual amount of face-to-face conversation.

Towards the end of the first year the baby starts to say his first proper words. He also shows that he understands several other words, as well as simple commands such as 'give it to Mummy' or 'where is the cup?' By two years he has a vocabulary of about fifty common words, mainly associated with his day-to-day life, though he obviously understands more.

Dean is fascinated by a picture of a zebra in a wildlife book, *far left*, but he is also picking up words and beginning to understand language as Annette talks him through the pictures. The process certainly works, because Gemma, looking at the book with Dean, *left*, now has a large vocabulary of more than two hundred words. She understands many more, though, and talks in short sentences of about five words.

A BORN IMITATOR

From about eight months, a baby enters a phase of imitation. He likes to watch what his mother does and now he wants to join in. He will watch someone sweeping, for example, and then sweep up himself with a handbrush, or dig in his own patch of earth while the flower beds are being weeded. He tries to help with feeding, by grabbing the spoon as it is on the way to his mouth.

At first, of course, the food is likely to end up smeared all over his face, but he should not be discouraged from trying to help and joining in – even though it makes mealtimes much longer. After all, it is his mouth and he is getting to the stage where he wants a say in what goes in and how it gets there.

An eight-month baby likes to be with his parents and to help them in their tasks. In this way he comes to understand what goes on in day-to-day life, and through imitation eventually works out how to do things himself. He learns by observing the behaviour of those around him and then copying it. In particular, a baby of this age enjoys games in which he imitates a partner. Hand clapping, peek-a-boo and pat-a-cake are all popular. He will also imitate some of the sounds of enjoyment that an adult makes.

As the baby becomes older, he becomes more aware of the world around him, and also more responsive to it. He understands his parents' tone of voice and some of the things that are said to him. He understands, for example, that when someone waves goodbye they are leaving, and that when a meal is being cooked it will soon be time to eat. He is watching, listening, copying and learning: he first learns how, and then, later, why particular activities are being carried out.

IMITATIVE PLAY
Try these tips for helping your baby:
- When you clean the house give him a duster to use, first making sure that he cannot break anything valuable.
- Let him sweep the floor with his own brush.
- When baking, give him a piece of pastry too.
- When you wash up the dishes, sit him on the floor with a bowl of warm, soapy water and a plastic beaker to wash up – but keep a careful eye on him.
- Let him dig a small patch in the garden and plant some seeds of his own.

Dean is learning how to play peek-a-boo, or, as Annette calls it, 'peep-oh', *above*, putting his hands in front of his face just as Annette has done. Annette has given him the lead, and by imitating her Dean works out how to play the game. Once learnt, Dean plays peek-a-boo over and over again, *above right* and *right*, uncovering one eye and then hiding it again. He loves this game and will play it repeatedly, grinning to show off six strong teeth.

DIARY 19TH JUNE

He's now playing peep-oh; he puts his hands up to his eyes and if you say, "Peep-oh", he laughs and covers up one eye. Then he looks for you to say it again and laughs more at your response. Sometimes he just plays the game on his own. He's also copying his sister so much – whatever she does, he tries to do it; if she's climbing up on the furniture, if she's running along on the pillows on the floor; if she laughs then he laughs. They are starting to play together so well.

ON TWO FEET

Before a baby can walk, he first has to discover how to stand upright. Until now he has either moved around on all fours or side-stepped along the furniture, steadying himself with his hands. Now he has to learn how to stand up on his own and balance independently without holding on to anything.

It sounds easier than it is. First, he has to raise himself from a squatting position, then maintain that position without toppling over. At first he tends to fall over backwards and lands with a bump on his bottom. Then, almost unbelievably, he stands alone for a few seconds, managing to stay upright a little longer on each subsequent day.

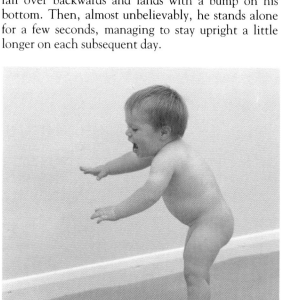

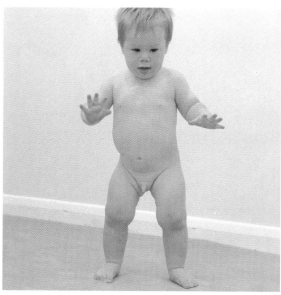

DIARY 22ND JULY

The other day he took four steps on his own so he's getting to the stage now where we think he might start walking, although he prefers to get from A to B on his knees because it's quicker. He will stand and balance for a few seconds but he seems to do it on his own terms – if we want him to stand he will sit down on his bottom. He will walk along just holding onto one hand, and he went for something on his own standing up, which I was thoroughly delighted with. He loves crawling up the stairs; if I leave him a few minutes he's gone up the stairs – but will he come down them feet first? No. Head first. He's a very determined little boy. He's a real explorer in the sense that he's got to be into everything and always knocking things down.

First, Dean raises himself carefully from a squat, *top*. This requires intense concentration, and the use of his arms as a balance to prevent him from falling over, *above left*. But eventually he succeeds, *above*, with his feet well apart to give him a broad base – though his knees still have a tendency to sag. Now Dean is ready to walk – but he feels a little insecure, and stretches his arms out for Annette to pick him up again, *right*.

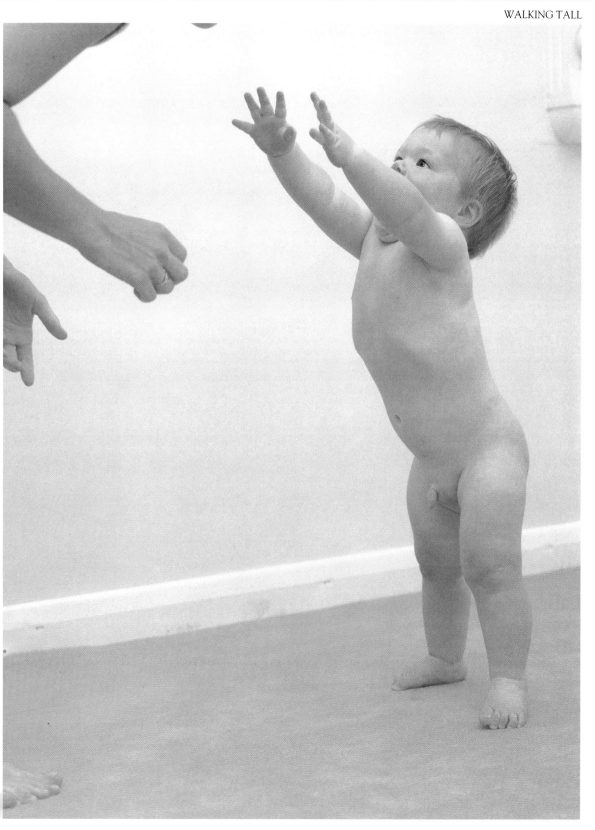

THE FIRST FEW STEPS

Once a baby can stand upright on his own without losing his balance and falling over, he is ready to start to walk. He already knows the basics, from tottering behind the wooden baby-walker (page 64), taking a few steps with his parents holding onto his hands, and from cruising along the furniture.

Now he has to take a step on his own. This really is a very complicated business for him, even though it may seem simple enough to us. He has to stand up on his feet, balance, then lift one foot up off the ground and place it down again in front of the other, while transferring his weight from one foot to the other. Then this process has to be repeated with the other foot. In the beginning he may be rather unsure of himself and need encouragement, reassurance and praise when he takes a step.

The first few steps are usually rather wobbly staggers with the arms flung out wide, the feet a good way apart and the legs sagging slightly at the knees and hips. This does not matter; there will be plenty of time to improve the technique later.

A baby should not be made to walk until he feels ready to do so and has demonstrated enough confidence to want to go it alone. It helps to practice indoors on a thick carpet, or outdoors on the lawn in summer, so that it does not hurt so much when he falls over – as he undoubtedly will. A carpet or lawn also means that he can learn to walk with bare feet, which helps his balance, though obviously he will need shoes later, when he begins to walk on different surfaces outside. At first he will feel happier walking a very short distance towards his mother or father, but when he is walking properly he will charge off in whatever direction takes his fancy.

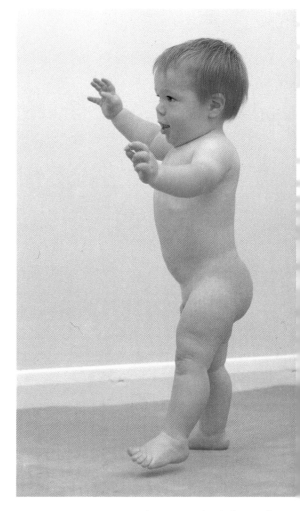

Dean has managed to balance, *above*, and has just taken a small step with his left foot. His weight is still on his right foot, though, and he will need to shift it to his left foot before taking the next step.

HELPING YOUR BABY WALK
- Choose a room with a good, thick carpet, but not one with long shag pile that might catch in his toes and trip him up.
- Watch how he gets up into a standing position.
- See how he steadies himself and gets his balance using his arms before attempting to set off.
- See if he normally sets off with his right foot.
- Watch him take a step, put his foot down and then transfer his weight onto it.
- Having taken the first step, watch him repeat the process with the other foot.
- Look at his expression: the fierce concentration, the surprise and frustration when he falls over and the pleasure when he gets it right and stays on his feet.
- Remember to encourage him.

Walking is a complicated process, and one that demands confidence on the part of the baby, so Annette has her hands close behind Dean, *right*, in order to reassure him that he is in no danger.

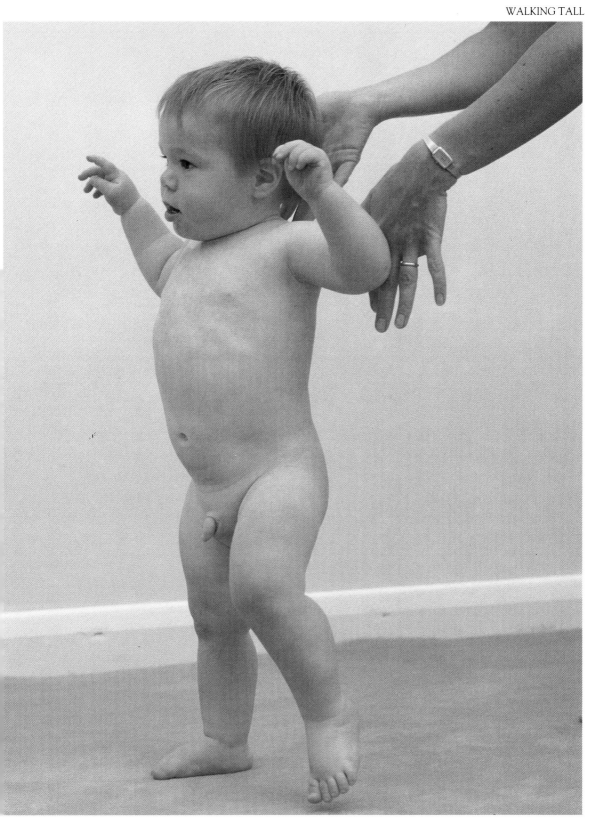

THE BIRTHDAY PARTY

A year old! A baby really deserves a celebration to mark his first birthday, not only because he has grown and learnt so much, but because he is healthy and strong. Nowadays we tend to take good health in babies for granted, but it was not always so. Years ago, the mortality rate at birth and during the first year was tragically high, but modern obstetric and paediatric care, together with immunization against diseases, has ensured that most babies thrive.

A party is a wonderful way of celebrating a birthday, and has the advantage that friends and relatives can join in, too. By a year, a baby will have sufficient understanding to know that something special is happening and that he is the centre of attention. He will love seeing his friends and grandparents, and have great fun opening his presents. The wrapping paper itself is likely to give as much pleasure as the contents of the parcels. That is not to say he will not appreciate any new toys, simply that he may be a little overwhelmed on the actual day. The toys can always be put away untouched and brought out at intervals later.

Jellies and biscuits

A first birthday party need not cost much, either in terms of time or money. Older babies like simple finger foods, jellies and biscuits, and lots of fun and games. Paper napkins, tablecloths and cups are both colourful and cheap and do not have to be washed up afterwards. The birthday cake itself need not be elaborate; very few children of this age like fruit cakes, so use a sponge mixture. Coloured icing and a few chocolate decorations turn even the plainest cake into a splendid sight, and one worthy of the occasion.

DIARY 10TH AUGUST

It was a bright, sunny day for Dean's birthday. Gemma was more excited than Dean about his birthday party and Dean found the sudden arrival of nine other children, as well as his respective grandparents, all a bit bewildering. He received some lovely presents, of which Gemma opened the majority, as Dean could only cope with pulling bows and he didn't really seem to understand that all the presents were specially for him.

Although he looked fairly dazed most of the time, Dean had a good day and certainly enjoyed all the food – his appetite was not deterred. He slept very deeply that night and so did Gemma.

Dean's two grandmothers enjoy the birthday party as much as he does, *below*. Having grandparents who live nearby is a great advantage, because they can act as child-minders and baby-sitters; for their part, grandparents can enjoy all the fun of a young child, without the day-to-day responsibility for bringing him up. They're very good at wiping noses, too, *bottom*, though Dean seems to prefer his new car.

One of Dean's presents is a bright, plastic tip-up truck, *right*, though he needs a little help from Jason to find out how it works. Even more mysterious and exciting is the beautifully wrapped present, *below*. What is inside it? Dean is determined to find out, and as he is now dextrous enough to be able to undo the bow, he stands a good chance of finding out very soon.

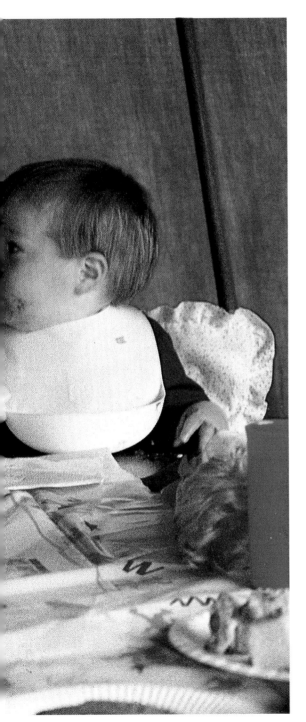

If it is a fine day it is a good idea to have the party in the garden or at least allow all the children to play out-of-doors. This has the advantage of cutting down on the amount of mess inside the house; but, on the other hand, means that there have to be enough adults to supervise play and make sure that there are no accidents. The older children may like to play organized games, such as blind man's buff or hide and seek, while younger ones will probably be happier playing by themselves with toys.

It is all great fun, of course, but it does have a learning side, too. Occasions such as this help Dean to develop social skills, adding to his store of knowledge by showing him how to interact with groups and form relationships with others.

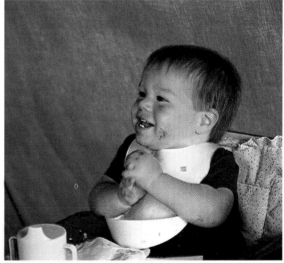

Dean loved everything about his party: his presents, his friends, and – above all – the ability to smear his face and everything else with chocolate, *above*. Dean's young friend seems very impressed indeed by Annette's splendid birthday cake, *left*, though Dean himself looks slightly quizzical. But the cake is superb: made to look like a fairground carousel, it has lots of brightly coloured marzipan animals on the top.

CHAPTER SIX

THE GROWING CHILD

Even though babies learn a great deal during their first year of life, they are nowhere near ready to live an independent life – unlike many other animals. In fact, it will be at least another twelve years or so before a baby begins to mature sexually and a good few years after that before he can begin to look after himself and work to support himself financially. It is a long childhood – a longer time than that for any other animal.

Over the past year the baby has developed both his gross and fine motor skills. At birth, his musculature was poorly developed: he was fairly floppy and entirely helpless. First, he gained control of his head, so that he could lift it off the ground and look around. Over the next year he learnt to sit up, then to crawl and eventually took his first few steps by himself. Tiny hands that started out as clenched fists became able to pick things up, explore nooks and crannies and point things out.

First crying, then cooing to babbling, he has learnt how to say a few words and shows that he understands many more. He knows what the purpose of his hairbrush is, for example, and will pick it up to brush his hair even though he cannot yet say hairbrush.

So he knows a lot already. He has assimilated the information by watching and listening, primarily to his mother, but also to other members of the family. It is a huge amount of information to amass and organize, but soon there will be even more, as he learns to run, skip and jump, to draw pictures, and to read and write as he develops his understanding of the world around him.

Dean is investigating the possibilities of a large daisy he has found in the garden, *left*. He holds it in his hands, twisting it this way and that so that he can examine it from all angles. He has pulled a couple of the white petals off and has worked out that he can take a flower to bits like this; but Dean is just about to discover that he cannot put it back together again, as he can with his toys.

ANIMAL MAGIC

Some babies are lucky enough to grow up in a house with a pet, and come to accept the animal as part of the family. At first they may well tend to ignore it most of the time, but usually they will become firm friends. For others, the first time they play with an animal is a fascinating experience. How can anything that small and furry and soft be alive? They may also be a bit frightened, particularly if a dog barks loudly or if they are scratched by a cat.

At first the baby may be a bit rough with the animal as he does not understand the need to be gentle. On the whole, dogs and cats put up with these indignities fairly well and do not retaliate. But very old animals and those nursing their own young may be a bit irritable with noisy, rough, young children, so all contacts should be supervised.

PRECAUTIONS WITH ANIMALS

- It is generally a bad idea to leave animals and babies together alone at any time. The animal may be irritable or jealous and may bite or scratch the child. Apart from the immediate problem this presents, it may also make the child afraid of animals in the future.
- Babies sleeping in prams and cots should be protected by cat nets. Some cats like to sleep on top of their owners, and a small baby would be unable to dislodge a large cat who happened to settle down to sleep upon his face.
- Animals should be kept clean and wormed regularly. Fleas and mites can cause skin rashes. The garden should be cleared of any excrement if children are going to play in it.

Dean loves playing outdoors. The garden provides him with marvellous opportunities for exploring, testing and tasting, *top*; and Dean and Gemma have plenty of space to have fun and games with the family cat, *above*.

Dean has learnt that kittens like being stroked, *right*, rather than mauled. In the beginning, he was rather rough, not realizing that the kitten was quite so young and delicate. Surprisingly, it did not attempt to run away, nor did it hiss or scratch him.

PLAYING GAMES

Having bravely taken those first, few, terrifying steps, a baby quickly gains in confidence. Over the next few months, he becomes steadier on his feet and his balance improves. His steps become more even, he starts to walk with his feet closer together, without having to rely on his arms for balance. Now he is able to turn his head and look at other things instead of looking where he is going – which tends to lead to the odd fall or bump.

In about six months time he will try to run and, inevitably, fall forward on to his outstretched hands. The top half of his body seems to be able to move forward faster than his legs will carry him. Eventually

Dean loves playing with a football, *left*. Here he looks very stylish indeed, but it is just an illusion. In fact, he has not been walking for very long and is still rather shaky on his legs; he walks with a broad base and needs to use his arms for balance, especially when starting to run down a slight slope, *above*. At this age he cannot yet kick the ball properly, but he can make it move by barging into it.

he works out the problem, though – usually at about eighteen months – and manages to run forwards properly. However, he has to keep his eyes on the ground in front of him and is at first unable to change course to swerve around obstacles.

All the movements involved in running are complex, requiring strength, neuro-muscular coordination and a good sense of balance. A few months ago they would have been out of the question, but by the time he is two years old the baby will be extremely fleet of foot; much to the consternation of his parents who frequently have to chase after him.

Boys generally love ball games, and, by and large, they are better at them than girls. This may be because they can run faster than girls, but may also be the result of the way in which adults played with them when they were babies and young children. There is some evidence that adults react in different ways to male and female babies. Female babies are more likely to be soothed and petted gently, for example, while boy babies come in for more rough and tumble when being handled. Consequently, it is thought, boys grow up with better ball skills than girls, and are generally better at contact sports. That is not to say that girls cannot learn or be trained to play games such as football; simply that boys generally start off with a bit of an advantage.

By two years a toddler can throw a ball, though not with any great accuracy. About six months later, he is able to kick a large football without losing his balance and falling over. It takes a little longer to master the art of catching a ball, but by three years old a small child can usually catch a large ball thrown carefully into his outstretched arms.

DIARY 25TH AUGUST

Dean is well and truly established on his feet now, so much so that we went ahead and bought him a pair of shoes. His walking really took off whilst we were away last week, and he's actually improved by playing football. He enjoys kicking a ball around and his coordination in achieving this is amazing, I think. Of course, now that he is up on his feet, games with Gemma are much more exciting and they chase each other around the house with great delight.

WATCHING YOUR BABY PLAY

Babies are a joy to watch, especially when they are playing happily on their own and do not know you are watching them. You can join in, of course.

● Buy a large brightly coloured, plastic football.

● Leave the ball on the grass and watch him go after it, crawling, creeping and walking in his desire to get to it.

● Watch how he picks it up – stooping down, bending at the knees and almost falling over backwards.

● See how he lifts it up very carefully, in both hands. Now that he has managed to capture it, he will be determined not to drop it.

● Roll a fairly large ball and encourage him to chase it.

● With him sitting on the floor, legs spread apart, roll the ball into his lap. Then ask him to roll it back to you.

● Give him a cardboard box and two or three small balls to drop into and pick up out of the box. He could practise dropping the balls and watching them bounce.

● Give him a ball and ask him to throw it back to you. He will almost certainly throw wildly – even behind him. This helps him to learn about letting objects go.

● Large, inflatable beach balls can be exciting. He will think that because of its size, the ball will be very heavy and therefore impossible for him to pick up.

Dean has spotted the ball, *far left*, and sets off in pursuit. He can walk but it is still sometimes quicker for him to crawl. Soon he has reached the ball, *above left*, and he wants to pick it up. Once on his feet, Dean squats down so that he can pick the ball up, *above*. Finally, he straightens up, clasps the ball firmly between his hands and forearms and starts to walk slowly across the lawn, *right*, concentrating hard so that he does not drop it.

Dean is now a sturdy young boy, and is becoming
increasingly confident on his feet. Here he is trying out a
new pair of sensible toddler's shoes in the garden. The
ground is a bit uneven, so he is using his arms to help him
balance and to prevent him stumbling. First he raises his
right foot and plants it down in front of his left foot, *below*,
then he transfers his weight from the left foot onto the right
foot, *near right*. He is just about to repeat the process, *middle
right*, when something startles him, interrupting his
concentration. Startled, he looks up, *far right*, with his
right foot in mid-air.

PLAYING WITH MOTHER

However grown-up and independent he might seem, a one-year-old baby is nevertheless a very little boy in terms of maturity. In spite of having learnt to walk, he still needs a lot of care and attention.

He may be brave enough to explore the back garden and get into all sorts of mischief, but he is still very attached to his mother and needs her approval and encouragement. He likes her to be around, particularly when he is trying out anything new, and will turn back to her when he feels unsure of himself and needs a hug. He is both affectionate and mischievous.

Toddlers love to play games with their parents, particularly those that involve singing and movement. They will join in with the fun and noise even though they do not know the words properly – just making a happy, tuneful noise does just as well. They will ask to be picked up by stretching out their arms when parents approach, but can usually manage to stand up by themselves, so the gesture is really a request for a reassuring cuddle, or perhaps a sign that they want to be carried for a while.

Moods

One-year-old babies know what they like and decide on their own what they want to do, and can make their wishes understood perfectly well. But they do not always realize that they cannot achieve precisely what they want, everytime. So they become upset and moody if they are stopped from doing what they want – being uncooperative about dressing and feeding, for example.

As yet they are too young to have any serious

tantrums and these moods do not last for long. Parents should continue to be loving and supportive even though their babies may seem unbearably irritating at these times. Soon the normal happy disposition returns and they go back to play, seemingly without a care in the world.

Dean enjoys noisy, physical games such as singing and rowing the boat, *above right*, with himself as the boat, and Annette's presence reassures him that he is not really in any danger. Another game Dean enjoys is an unusual variation on blind man's buff, *right*, in which Annette has to avoid serious injury to win!

Toddlers always like to be sure that their mother is around, and frequently ask for a cuddle. Dean is a bit tired, *left*, so he is holding out his arms to ask Annette to carry him for a while. Soon they have started another game, *below* – Annette holds Dean's hands so that he can bounce up and down without falling over.

SAFETY FIRST

It is lovely to watch a toddler acquiring new skills, but climbing, in particular, means that parents must be ever-vigilant to make sure that there are no accidents.

● Fit gates at the top and bottom of the stairs so that he cannot go up and down unless you are there.

● Make sure that any outside stairs, or stairs in the garden, are made safe as well.

● Make sure that he cannot reach anything dangerous or breakable from his vantage point on the furniture – both in the kitchen, where kettles and saucepans can be a hazard, and in the drawing room, where there may be china ornaments.

● It is no longer safe to keep medicines and household cleaners on a high shelf. Store them in cupboards, and fit childproof locks. Remember that he will soon be able to open the fridge, so either lock it or make sure that its contents are harmless.

● Never leave him alone to play in the bathroom, or sitting in the bath. He could easily drown, or he might scald himself if he turns the hot water on.

● Walk round the house, noting any potential danger points. Obviously you cannot turn your home into a fortress on account of one inquisitive toddler, but you must take all reasonable precautions.

DIARY 25TH AUGUST

Dean is into climbing onto everything, anything and everything. We have some tree stumps in the back garden and he climbs onto those; he climbs up the steps of the slide and down the steps; he'll watch his sister and try anything that she's done. He gets on the trampoline, he gets on the bike; he loves climbing up and exploring. He also falls very well.

Dean is just beginning to discover the wonderful world of chairs. At the moment, he needs to use a small box to reach the chair, *above left*, but soon he is up, twisting himself round to see what is going on, *above*. It is quite an achievement, and Dean looks appropriately pleased with himself. Getting down is never as easy as climbing up, *right*. Here Dean is warily lowering himself on to his toes, while clinging to the arms of the chair for support. The fact that he is holding on to a wooden hammer with one hand makes everything that bit more difficult, but he certainly does not want to let it go.

CLIMBING

A young toddler becomes increasingly more mobile during his second year. He starts to walk with confidence and skill, and becomes better at things like stopping and starting and negotiating corners. He learns how to run properly, concentrating hard, watching the ground in front of him and using his arms for balance. And he discovers climbing.

Stairs
At first, his climbing activities are limited to cautiously creeping up the stairs – unless this is prevented by a gate at the bottom. Once up, he is usually marooned, unable to get down again, and cries for help. He soon learns to come down backwards, though – slowly, step by step and using both his hands and his feet. Coming down forwards is much more difficult, until he learns how to pause and sit down on each step on the way. But by about eighteen months, most toddlers can walk up and down the stairs when held by the hand; and by two years they get up and down the stairs on their own, usually by holding on to the banister and putting both feet on every stair.

Sometime during the second year, toddlers learn how to climb up onto an armchair. They regard this as a tremendous achievement, and are usually terribly pleased with themselves when they succeed. This is because up until this point, the armchairs have seemed part of a different world, and one in which they want to share. Now they can take part – and also, of course, they can climb on to their parents' laps for a cuddle. From now on, there will be no stopping them from rampaging around the furniture – so it is important to keep a close eye on them.

Dean likes to practise his manipulative skills on a piece of play-dough, *above*. It is soft, springy and changes shape in a very satisfying way when he squeezes it. Play such as this helps him learn how to tackle more complex jobs, such as fastening the buckle on his shoe, *top right*. He still has not mastered the buckle, but Jason is encouraging him to persevere.

Drawing is great fun, even if all that Dean can produce so far is a scribble. At first he tries to hold the crayon in his left hand, *bottom right*, without much success. Realizing that he has two hands to use, he transfers the crayon to his right hand, *far right*, with better results.

HANDIWORK

At one year, a toddler is becoming increasingly clever and adept with his hands. He can hold two bricks, one in each hand, and bang them together in front of him, and he may be able to stack them into a tower of two or even three bricks, once he has seen a demonstration. He can also point with his index finger and pick up very small objects between his forefinger and thumb – this can be done with either hand, though usually one is preferred. He will hold a crayon in a rather awkward whole-handed grasp, using either or both hands, and scribble on a sheet of paper.

Generally, toddlers like to help with dressing and try to untie shoe-laces or pull off their socks, though sometimes they become moody and refuse to help.

DIARY 25TH AUGUST

When he is not tearing around investigating and exploring, Dean will sit happily for a short time playing with toys and objects. If you give him a brush he will brush his hair and similarly, he knows what a comb is for. He's also started to put things into one another; he loves knocking over building beakers and then trying to fit them into each other; normally the large one into the small one, but the intention is there. We've now dispensed with the baby toys as these never really interested him; he didn't enjoy rattles and squeaky things.

CAUSE AND EFFECT

As the months go by, a toddler becomes more and more confident about walking. He no longer has to use his arms for balance, and this allows him to carry something in each hand, push a small pram or cart in front of him, or trail a toy behind him. He can stoop down to pick up a toy without falling over, but he is not so good at sitting down, tending to collapse backwards onto his bottom with a bump. He is also acquiring what is called 'definition through use'. This means that even though he cannot pronounce an object's name properly, he knows and understands what it is used for – and demonstrates this knowledge by trying to put it to that use.

Although Dean is much steadier on his feet, he still falls over fairly often, *above left*, usually when he is attempting something that is just a little bit too difficult. Here he has tried to kick the ball, though few toddlers can do this until they are about two years old. He keeps trying, however, *above top*, this time with a shoe in each hand. After this he has a go at helping with the cleaning, *above*. It is an amusing example of definition by use – he knows that brushes are used for brushing hair, but does not yet understand that there are different brushes for different purposes.

Dean is just about to fall over backwards on to his bottom, *above*, as toddlers tend to do. He has not got his centre of gravity in quite the right place to both pick up the truck and stay on his feet. But there are other, less subtle, games that he can enjoy – such as trying to burst a ball with a wooden hammer, *left*. Great fun!

A DAY OUT

Expeditions are always fun, especially when they involve something new and exciting. Toddlers become bored by the familiar routines and like nothing better than to be out exploring a new activity or place. It can be a trip to the swings in the local park, a ride on a shiny red bus or a swim in the pool. But an outing to the zoo is a real treat, because it gives a toddler a chance to compare the pictures in his books with the real thing. In this way he can begin to learn about wild animals and where they come from – to get the beginnings of an idea of the size and possibilities of the world.

Dean is fascinated by an elegant crane, with lovely grey feathers and long legs, *above*. Unfortunately, the crane is less keen on Dean, and is just about to give his fingers a nip.

Gemma noticed what the crane had done, and thinking that Dean may be upset, *left*, gives him a reassuring kiss and a cuddle – just as she has seen Annette do so many times before.

In spite of being pecked, Dean has enjoyed his day, *below*. He has revelled in the exotic sights, the strange sounds and the unusual smells, and wants to come again.

DIARY 3RD SEPTEMBER

Today we went to Farnham Birdworld and Dean was on his feet for a large percentage of the time. He was running about, amazed and dumbfounded by all the birds; he kept pointing and making noises of glee. When we first got there he went up to one bird and stuck his fingers through the fence and it bit him, but he didn't show any signs of being frightened; I expect it's because he's used to Gemma biting him so a bird was fairly tame. Gemma's reaction was one of horror and crying on Dean's behalf, so we had to explain to her that it didn't really hurt Dean or else he would have cried.

THE JOYS TO COME

During the second year, a toddler gains both in confidence and experience. He already possesses all the skills he needs to get around, play with his toys and help with dressing and feeding – now all he needs to do is practise them and refine them. Over the next year or so, he will learn to run and climb with growing assurance and competence.

By two, toddlers can throw a ball – albeit rather inaccurately – but cannot catch. This takes rather longer to learn, and few children can manage it until they are over three, though boys seem to be able to pick up the knack more quickly than girls.

Fine manipulative skills steadily improve as well. By about eighteen months, a toddler can build a tower of three bricks, and by two years the tower can be as many as six or seven bricks high. All toddlers love scribbling with a pencil or crayon, and gradually become more and more adept, so that by two-and-a-half years they can copy the letters O, T and V.

Vocabulary gradually increases as well: at the beginning of the year, a toddler can understand a number of common words and say one or two of them; but by the end of the second year he understands a large number of words and can use around fifty of them in their correct context.

And so the process continues: always watching, learning, experimenting and savouring new experiences, a child grows, slowly but surely, in both body and mind. Before one knows it, the toddler is a sturdy child, becoming ever more confident and prepared to take on the challenges and the rough and tumble of everyday life. Looking back, he will hardly believe that, like Dean, he was once tiny, defenceless and dependent. But the evidence is here.

Playgrounds are wonderful places, full of roundabouts, swings and slides – the faster they go, the more children seem to like them. Nowadays Dean has the confidence and personality to express his own wishes; he has decided that the roundabout looks good fun, and cannot wait to join in. Unfortunately, all the places on this roundabout are taken, so he will have to wait his turn – a difficult concept for a toddler to understand.

CHART YOUR BABY'S STORY

On these last pages there are charts for you to record readily observable aspects of your own baby's development. Since no two babies are exactly alike, there are bound to be differences in their rate of development. Some babies will do some things ahead of time, and others will take a few weeks longer to attain certain skills. It follows that there is obviously a period of time (often a few months), during which the majority of healthy babies will begin to achieve a particular skill. This is the normal range, and this is the range which has been quoted throughout the book. On the chart opposite, space is provided for you to indicate the date at which your baby reached each developmental milestone. The charts overleaf record normal ranges of development for height, weight and teeth.

If, for any reason, you are seriously worried about your baby's development, seek medical advice without delay. If there is a problem, prompt diagnosis and treatment can do nothing but good and will minimize any developmental delay.

DEVELOPMENTAL STAGES	DATE OBSERVED
Newborn to one month • Head flops back when pulled to sit, and droops forward when held under tummy, **a.** • Grasp, rooting or suckling, Moro or startle reflex, and stepping reflexes are present, **b.** • By one month baby starts to move arms and legs jerkily; head can be held erect for a moment; fists clenched most of the time, **c.** • Fixes gaze on close object and eyes follow its movement, **d.** • Watches mother closely. May smile when sees mother's face or hears her voice, **e.** • Makes small throaty noises, **f.**	a b c d e f
By three months • Baby has little head lag when pulled to sit. Held sitting, back is straight except at the bottom, **a.** • Brings hands together in front of face and plays with fingers, watching them intently, **b.** • Can briefly hold a toy placed in hands, **c.** • Held standing on a flat surface, legs sag at the knees. • Visually alert and interested; quietens and smiles for mother, **e.** • Makes lots of sounds: cooing, chuckling and squealing, but loud noises can distress, **f.**	a b c d e f
By six months • Back and neck can be held straight when in a sitting position; may be able to sit alone for a short time, **a.** • Baby rolls over; first from front to back, later from back to front, **b.** • Can now confidently reach out with hands to grasp an object or toy seen, **c.** • Grasps objects in the palm of hand and can transfer them from one hand to the other, **d.** • Takes everything to mouth, **e.** • Makes lots of noise: laughs when happy and screams when cross, **f.**	a b c d e f

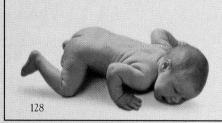

DEVELOPMENTAL STAGES	DATE OBSERVED	IMMUNIZATION

DEVELOPMENTAL STAGES

By nine months
- Can sit independently on the floor, **a.**
- Moves about a great deal, squirming along the floor or by crawling on hands and knees, **b.**
- May be able to pull body up to a standing position holding the furniture, **c.**
- Picks up small objects between first finger and thumb in a pincer grasp; tries to grasp spoon when being fed, **d.**
- Plays peek-a-boo and imitates hand clapping games; enjoys ringing bell, **e.**
- Can say 'Dada' and 'Mama' and usually understands 'no' and 'bye-bye', **f.**

By one year
- Starts to side-step or cruise around the furniture, holding on with hands, **a.**
- May be able to stand alone and take a few independent steps, **b.**
- Uses both hands but may favour one, **c.**
- Pokes and points at desired objects or happenings with index finger, **d.**
- Understands a number of words, knows own name, and will obey simple instructions, **e.**
- Very affectionate; does not like being separated from mother and father; still quite wary of strangers, **f.**

By fifteen months
- Walks alone with feet wide apart and arms held out to help balance, **a.**
- Sits down by collapsing backwards onto bottom with a bump, **b.**
- Creeps upstairs step by step, and sometimes can come down again, usually backwards, **c.**
- Scribbles with crayons on paper, likes books, stories and pictures, **d.**
- Eating well; drinks from a cup; holds own spoon, brings it to mouth and sometimes eats from it, **e.**

DATE OBSERVED

By nine months: a, b, c, d, e, f

By one year: a, b, c, d, e, f

By fifteen months: a, b, c, d, e

IMMUNIZATION

Fill in your baby's immunization dates on this chart. Remember that immunizations should not be given if your baby is unwell or has a high temperature. After an injection the baby may be a bit grizzly for a day or so.

Children with epilepsy or other neurological disorders should not be given Pertussis (Whooping cough) immunization.

3 months: First Triple; Diptheria, Tetanus and Pertussis plus Oral Polio vaccine

_____

5 months: Second Triple immunization and Oral Polio

_____

9 months: Third Triple immunization and Oral Polio

_____

15 months: Measles, Mumps and Rubella combined immunization

_____

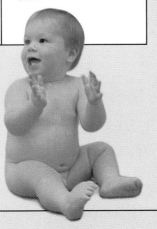

GROWTH CHARTS

Newborn babies are always weighed and measured at birth. Indeed, it is usually one of the first questions friends and relatives ask – once they have found out whether it was a boy or girl. How much did baby weigh? Babies continue to be weighed and measured throughout their first year of life. Their weight and height is recorded on a chart and compared with their previous measurements, and the average weight and height for a baby of the same age. In this way, any failure to gain weight or height can be spotted at an early stage and the reasons for it investigated. Examples of these growth charts are displayed here for you to use.

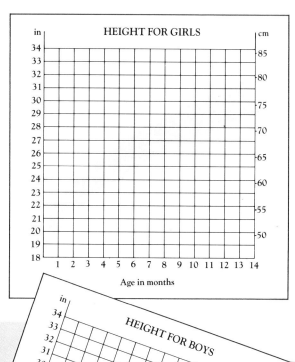

HEIGHT FOR GIRLS

Age in months

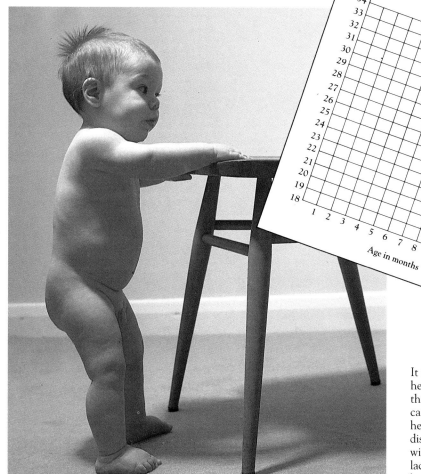

HEIGHT FOR BOYS

Age in months

It is important to measure a child's height, or, in the case of a small baby, their length when lying down. This can be plotted on a chart of average heights, *above*, and any great discrepancy noted. A few children will fail to grow properly because they lack growth hormone. This can now be given by injection provided the problem is spotted at an early age.

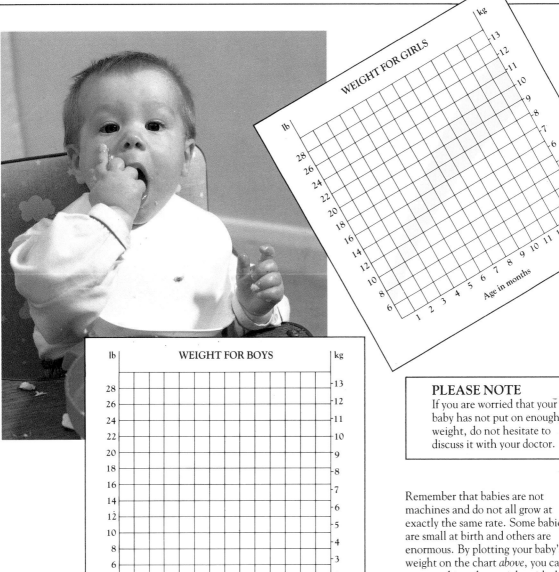

WEIGHT FOR GIRLS

lb
28
26
24
22
20
18
16
14
12
10
8
6

kg
13
12
11
10
9
8
7
6
5
4
3
2

Age in months
1 2 3 4 5 6 7 8 9 10 11 12 13 14

lb	WEIGHT FOR BOYS	kg

lb
28
26
24
22
20
18
16
14
12
10
8
6

kg
13
12
11
10
9
8
7
6
5
4
3
2

Age in months
1 2 3 4 5 6 7 8 9 10 11 12 13 14

PLEASE NOTE
If you are worried that your baby has not put on enough weight, do not hesitate to discuss it with your doctor.

Remember that babies are not machines and do not all grow at exactly the same rate. Some babies are small at birth and others are enormous. By plotting your baby's weight on the chart *above*, you can compare his or her weight with that of many other babies as the chart shows standard values based on the measurements of a large population.

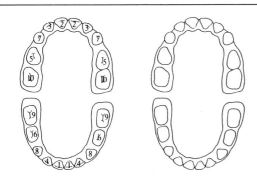

These dental diagrams show the order in which the first, or milk teeth usually appear. As with everything else in child development, there is a good deal of variation from one baby to another. You can fill in the order that your baby's teeth appear in the empty spaces, *left*.

Generally, the bottom two incisors appear first at about six months or so, followed by the two top teeth. Thereafter, two more teeth appear in the lower jaw and so on until by the end of the first year the baby often has eight teeth. Between two and two-and-half years the baby has a complete set of teeth.

131

FURTHER READING

Asher, Jane. *Keep Your Baby Safe* Penguin Books, London 1981

Carter, Margaret (Ed). *Baby's First Year of Life* Oxford Illustrated Press, Somerset 1983

Carter, Margaret (Ed). *Good Housekeeping Baby Book* Ebury Press, London 1985

Donaldson, Margaret. *Children's Minds* Fontana, London 1984

Einon, Dorothy. *Parenthood: The Whole Story* Bloomsbury, London 1988

Harvey, Dr David (Consul. Ed) *New Parents* Hamlyn Books, London 1988

Jolly, Hugh. *Book of Child Care: Complete Guide for Today's Parents* Allen & Unwin, London 1985

Kovar, Dr Ilya. *Make it Better* Octopus Books, London 1983

Leach, Penelope. *Baby and Child* Penguin Books, London 1980

Lloyd, E. Messenger, M. Scheffler, A. *Baby Language* Unwin Paperbacks, London 1986

Raynor, Claire. *Baby and Young Child Care* Purnell Books, Maidenhead, Berks 1981

Sheridan, Mary *From Birth to Five Years: Children's Developmental Progress* NFER-Nelson Pub. Co., Windsor, Berks 1981

Sheridan, Mary. *Spontaneous Play in Early Childhood* NFER-Nelson Pub. Co., Windsor, Berks 1977

Stoppard, Dr Miriam. *The Baby Care Book* Dorling Kindersley Ltd, London 1988

Tizard, Barbara, Hughes, Martin. *Young Children Learning* Fontana Original, London 1984

Welford, Heather. *The A-Z of Feeding in the First Year* Unwin Hyman,Ltd London 1988

INDEX

Page numbers in bold refer to photographs

A

allergy 50
amniotic fluid 18
antibodies **11**
anti-fungal cream 18
apple 54, 56
arms **14**, 24, 39, **74**, 84, 100, 128
attention 20, **22**, 45, 66, 72, **72**, 73
awareness 68

B

baby
    oil 19
    seat 28, 39
    walker **65**, 90, 100
back 28, **28**, **29**, 39, **39**, 45, 128
balance 39, **39**, 45, 74, 80, 90,
    91, 98, **98**, 100, **100**, 111,
    111, 114, 119, 122, 129
ball 40, 76, **76**, 84, 111, **111**,
    112, **113**, **122**, 126
bathing 12, 19, **19**, 20, 22, 40,
    45, 86
bathroom 118
beads 93
bell **59**, 84, 129
bilirubin 18
birth 10, 78
    canal 10, 18
    marks 18
birthday 102, **102**, 103, 105, **105**
blindness 76
blinking 14, 76
blood 10, 18
bonding 46
bones 18
books 40, 84, **95**, 129
bottle-feeding 13, 34, 50
bread 55
breast
    -feeding 10, **11**, 13, 34, **34**, 45, 46
    milk 13, 34, 50
breathing 10, 13
bricks 40, **41**, **47**, 60, 84, 93, 121
    building with 60, 84, 121, 126

C

Caesarian section 18
calcium 57
calorie requirement 50
caput 18
car seat 75
carrot 54
cat 108, **108**
catching 40, 111, 126
changing mat 36, 59
cheeks 18
chewing 34, 50, 53, 56, 66
childproof locks 66, 74, 118
children, older 20, **20**, 46, 49,
    59, 72, 78
choking 54
climbing 80, **80**, 118, **118**, 119,
    126
    frame 80
colostrum **11**
colour vision 30, 33
communication 12, **43**, 60, 68,
    68, 95
confidence 20, 22, 36, **43**, 68, 70,
    100, **100**, 111, **114**, 119, 122,
    126
control, of body *See* neuro-
    muscular control
cradle cap 18
crawling 36, 37, 39, 40, 45, **45**,
    64, **65**, 66, **66**, 70, 74, **74**, 75,
    81, 83, 90, 98, 106, 112, **113**,
    129
cruising 65, 74, 83, 90, 100, 129
crying 10, 12, 13, 20, **47**, **55**, 95,
    106
cuddling 12, 20, **20**, 30, 40, 45,
    45, 73, 116, **117**, 119, **125**
cupboards 66, 74, 118
curiosity **26**, 30, 59, 66, 86

D

deafness 95
definition through use 122, **122**
delivery 8, **9**, 18, 46
dentist 57

E

dexterity 92–93, **93**, 103
diet 50, 53, 57
discrimination 68
dog 80, 108
drawing 106, **120**
dressing 40, 45, 84, 116, 121, 126
dummy 57

E

ears 95
earth 80, 96
egocentricity *See* self-obsession
epidural anaesthetic 10
episiotomy 10
experience 59, 68, 126
exploring 60, 65, 83, 84, 93, 98,
    108, 116, 118, 121, 124
eyelids 18
eyes **9**, 28, 76
    colour 18
eyesight *See* sight

F

face 19
    mother's **9**, 20, 30, **30**, 32, 46,
    76, 128
falling, risk of 36
family 42, 46, 49, 54, 66, 72, 87,
    108
fat 16
father 12, 46, **47**, **49**
feeding 10, 11, 12, 13, 20, **20**, 22
    30, 34, 42, 46, 52, 54, 66, 84,
    96, 116, 126, 129
    battles over 54
    bowl **52**, 53
    cup 49, 54, 55, **55**, 84
feet 39, 45, 64, **74**, 100, **100**,
    114, 129
fetal position 26
fingers 24, **24**, 39, 40, 76, 84, 92,
    93, 121, 128
fires 74
fist 24, 39, 45, 92, 106, 128
fleas 108
flotation aids 86, **86**, 88, **88**

focus 30, **30**, **31**
formula feeds 34, 50
friends 45, 49, 86, 102, **105**, 108

G

games 68, 84, **85**, 96, **96**, 97,
   105, 111, 116, **116**, **117**, **123**
garden 80, 105, **107**, 108, **108**,
   114, 116, 118
gates 66, 74, 118, 119
German measles 95
glands 18
glucose 10
grandparents 102, **102**
grasp 14, **14**, 24, **25**, 28, 39, 40,
   41, 45, 76, 92, 93, 128

H

haemoglobin 18
hair 16, 18, 22, 86
hand-eye coordination 24, 32,
   40, 54
hands **14**, 22, 24, **24**, **25**, 32, 39,
   45, 56, **66**, **70**, 74, **74**, 76, 83,
   92, 106, 128, 129
head 18, 20, 22, 39, 45
   control **22**, 26, **26**, 28, **28**, **29**,
      31, 106, 128
hearing 31, 32, 33, 95
   range 32
heart 10, 34
helping 96, **122**
hormone 10, 46
hunger 12, 13, **47**, 55

I

imagination 40
imitation 68, **68**, 84, 85, 95, 96,
   96, 97, 129
incisor 56, 131

J

jaundice 18
jaw 34, 53, 56

jealousy 12, 20, 31, 46, 49, 72,
   108
joint-position sense *See*
   proprioreception
jumping 106

K

kicking 22, 26, 28, 39, **45**, **70**
   a ball 40, 111, **111**, **122**
knees 39, **64**, **70**, **74**, 128, 129
knives 75

L

language 42, 60, 66, 95, **95**
lanugo 16
learning 20, 22, **24**, 30, 32, 36,
   39, 40, **41**, 45, 49, 66, 68, **68**,
   73, 84, 92, **93**, 96, 106
legs **14**, 22, 36, 39, 45, **70**, 84,
   128
lips **24**
liver 18
lumbar curve **22**, 28
lungs 8, 10

M

make-believe 40
matches 75
mealtimes 45, 54, 96
medicines 74, 118
memory 59, 83
midwife 10, **10**
milk 10, **11**, 13, 34, 50, 53, 54
   cow's 12, 50
   soya 50
   spots 18
mirror 59, **59**, 84
mites 108
mobiles 33, 40
molars 57
moods 116, 121
Moro **14**, 128
moulding 18
mouth 10, **24**, 30, 33, 39, 45, 50,
   55, 56, **66**, 84, 96

mouthing 41, 45
muscles 26, 34, 53, 106
music 40

N

name 45
nappy 36, 56
   changing 12, 18, 20, 28, 36,
      39, 40, **81**
   rash 18
neck 18, 26, 28
needs, of a baby 12
negativism 83
nerves **10**
nervous system 14
neuro-muscular control 22, 28,
   74, 111
nose 10, 18, **72**, 83

O

overdue babies 16
oxytocin 10

P

paddling pool 84, **85**
pants, plastic 18
pets 108
Piaget 59–60
pictures 76, 84, **95**, 129
pillow 13
pincer grasp 76, 92, 129
placenta 10
plasticine 84
plastic pots 93
play-dough 84, **120**
playing 20, 22, 24, 31, 36, 39,
   40, **41**, 46, 49, **60**, 63, 65, 66,
   72, 80, **80**, 84, 85, 87, 96, **96**,
   97, 105, **108**, 111, **111**, 112,
   116, **120**, 121, 126
power points 74
pram 39
preferences 83–84, 116
premature babies 16

problem solving 40
proprioception 32

R
rash **17**, 108
rattle **25**, 32, **32**, 33, 40, 45, 46, 121
reaching 24, **24**, 32, **32**, 33, 39, 40, **41**, 45, **50**, 76, 92
reading 40, 42, 106
reasoning 59–60
reflexes 14, 92, 128
rolling over 36, 37, 39, 45, 65, 128
routine 12, 13, 20, 124
running 40, 106, 111, **111**, 119, 126
rusks 45, **50**

S
sandpit 83, **83**
scalp 18
scissors 75
scribbling 40, 76, 84, **120**, 121, 126, 129
self-obsession 59, 60
shaking 45
sharing 40, 49, 72
shoulders 26, **26**, 28, 31
sight 20, 30, **30**, 31, **31**, 33, 40, 76, **76**
singing 116, **116**
sitting **22**, 28, **28**, **29**, 36, 39, 45, 65, 106, 121, 122
sixth sense *See* proprioception
skin 16–19, 34, 108
skipping 40, 106
skull 18
sleep 12, 13, 20, 26, 45
sliding 80, 83
sling 28
smell, sense of 32, 34, 59
smiling 20, 59, 83, 128
socializing 40, 49, 68, 105
solid food 34, **34**, 45, 50, 53-54, 56

spatial relationships 60
spoiling 12, 20
spoon 84, 96, 129
spots **17**, 18, 19
stairs 66, 74, 98, 118, 119
standing **43**, 64, 65, 74, 80, 83, 90, **91**, 98, 100, 116
startle reflex *See* Moro
stepping reflex **14**, 128
stimulation 66
Stork's Beak 18
strawberry naevi 18
sucking **24**, 39, **39**, **45**, 53
suckling 10, 34, 128
swaddling **11**
swallowing 33, 45, 54
swimming 86, **86**, 87, 88, **88**
swinging **78**, 80

T
talking 20, 31, 42, **43**, 59, 68, 83, 95, **95**, 106, 126
tantrums 19, 20, 49, 72, 116
taste, sense of 32, 54
teaching 46, 78
teddy bear **33**, 40
teeth 34, 45, 50, 53, 54, 56, **78**, 96, 131
brushing 57
teething 39, **39**, **45**, 54, 56
tooth care 57
throwing 111, 112, 126
thrush 18
thumb 24, 92, 121
sucking **24**, 39, 45, 49, 64
tickling 40, **72**
tinned food 54
toast 54
toes **14**, 39, **39**, 45
tongue **24**
touch, sense of **26**, 32, 59
Toxacara canis 80
toys 33, 39, 40, 45, 46, 49, **49**, 56, 59, 60, **63**, 65, 66, **66**, 72, 73, 76, 84, 92, 93, **93**, 102, 105, 121, 122, 126

U
ultra-violet light 18
umbilical cord 8, 10, **10**

V
Vaseline 19
ventral suspension 26
vernix 10, 16, 18
vision *See* sight
visual field 28, 45, 60, 76
visually associated reaching 32
vitamin D 57
voice 31, 45

W
waking 12, 13, 20, 45
walking 39, **65**, 74, 76, 90, 98, **98**, 100, **100**, 106, 111, **111**, 113, 119, 122
watching baby 36, 112, 118
water 68, 83, 84, 86, 88
wings 86, **86**, 88, **88**
waving 68, **68**, 96
weaning 32, 53–54
weight 34, 50, 130
wind 12
womb 10, 16, 18, **24**, 95
worms 80, 108
writing 42, 106

ACKNOWLEDGEMENTS

Creative Director Nick Eddison
Editorial Director Ian Jackson
Designer Amanda Barlow
Editor Christine Moffat
Index Michael Allaby
Production Bob Towell
Charts (pages 128–131) Anthony Duke
Composite make-up and retouching Ian Frost
Kingsway/Phillips Colour Laboratories